Leather Apparel
Design

Leather Apparel Design

FRANCESCA STERLACCI

Delmar Publishers

I**T**P® an International Thomson Publishing company

Albany • Bonn • Boston • Cincinnati • Detroit • London • Madrid
Melbourne • Mexico City • New York • Pacific Grove • Paris • San Francisco
Singapore • Tokyo • Toronto • Washington

NOTICE TO THE READER

Delmar Staff

Acquisitions Editor: Christopher Anzalone
Developmental Editor: Jeffrey D. Litton
Project Editor: Eugenia L. Orlandi
Production Coordinator: Jennifer Gaines
Art & Design Coordinator: Douglas J. Hyldelund
Editorial Assistant: Judy A. Roberts

COPYRIGHT © 1997
By Delmar Publishers
an International Thomson Publishing Inc.

The ITP logo is a trademark under license.

Printed in the United States of America

For more information, contact:

Delmar Publishers
3 Columbia Circle, Box 15015
Albany, New York 12212-5015

International Thomson Publishing–Europe
Berkshire House
168–173 High Holborn
London WC1V 7AA
England

Thomas Nelson Australia
102 Dodds Street
South Melbourne, 3205
Victoria, Australia

Nelson Canada
1120 Birchmount Road
Scarborough, Ontario
Canada M1K 5G4

International Thomson Editores
Campos Eliseos 385, Piso 7
Col Polanco
11560 Mexico D F Mexico

International Thomson Publishing GmbH
Konigswinterer Strasse 418
53227 Bonn
Germany

International Thomson Publishing–Asia
221 Henderson Road
#05–10 Henderson Building
Singapore 0315

International Thomson Publishing–Japan
Hirakawacho Kyowa Building, 3F
2-2-1 Hirakawacho
Chiyoda-ku, Tokyo 102
Japan

1 2 3 4 5 6 7 8 9 10 XXX 02 01 00 99 98 97 96

Library of Congress Cataloging-in-Publication Data
Sterlacci, Francesca.
    Leather apparel design / Francesca Sterlacci.
      p. cm.
    Includes bibliographical references and index.
    ISBN 0-8273-7772-X
    1. Leather garments. 2. Dressmaking. 3. Costume design.
I. Title.
TT524.S74   1997   96-17224
685'.22—dc20   CIP

Contents

Foreword

Many thousands of years ago, humankind discovered that animals could satisfy two of their three basic needs for survival: food, clothing, and shelter. Using the hides from the food the animals provided, humans covered themselves with the first clothing.

In the following millennia, many advancements were made in clothing materials—clothes are now made from wool, cotton, trees, and petrochemicals.

However, the leather apparel-making process has not changed much. Humans still make leather apparel from animal hides and skins, the by-products of food consumption. What *has* changed dramatically and dynamically is both the tanning process and the tremendous variety of available hides.

We can imagine that our cave-dwelling ancestors adorned themselves with fur-covered hides. Historically, humans have always felt the need for creative expression. They no doubt fashioned their first garments both for function, to protect themselves from the elements, and to broadcast their identity. Perhaps a wooly mammoth cape was a status symbol then, as are Gucci loafers today.

Throughout the ages, leather has had an allure, a cachet, unlike any other fabric. The words *genuine leather* evoke images of quality. We appreciate the elegance and workmanship of a finely bound leather book or a beautifully tanned leather handbag or briefcase.

Leather Apparel Design is the most complete textbook available on the subject, providing a thorough, comprehensive overview of the history and uses of tanned leather throughout the ages. The outline of the tanning process is extremely detailed, yet easily understood. This textbook provides a "how-to" guide that can be utilized by students and industry professionals for years to come.

—Jeanette Nostra, Executive Vice President, GIII Apparel Group, Ltd.
—Carl Katz, Executive Vice President, Siena Leather

Preface

My goal in writing this book was to create a comprehensive guide to designing leather garments. This book was written to appeal both to professionals who are currently involved in the fashion design business and students who have completed at least one year of degreed schooling in fashion design. However, anyone can read the book and learn a great deal, even if they have only a passing knowledge of fashion design.

Many of my students at The Fashion Institute of Technology and several other local schools with whom I am associated expressed an avid interest in learning more about leather apparel design. I was genuinely surprised to discover that no one had written a leather apparel design textbook specifically to educate both the serious design student or the professional already working in the leather apparel industry.

Thus, with this book, I hope more and more design schools will realize they now have an all-inclusive tool to expand their existing leather design program or to create a new one. I also hope the hundreds of leather apparel manufacturers around the world will use this book to help train their new employees regarding the jargon, techniques, and good judgment needed to create marketable leather garments.

This book educates the reader about the history of leather garments from prehistoric times to the present day. It illustrates, through a series of photographs, the changing face of leather garment design. The reader will learn about the evolution of the leather garment and also will become familiar with the designers who were, and are, influential in the leather apparel industry.

This book explains the leather tanning process in layperson's terms. It also introduces the reader to the terminology that is regularly used by professionals in the leather apparel industry. It also describes the various types of leather skins available for purchase around the world. It provides a definitive index of the characteristics, size, and end use for every type of skin, including exotic skins such as fish and hippopotamus. Students will probably be surprised at the vast array of available skins—by learning about these skins they will be better equipped to choose the appropriate skin for a particular design. The appropriate choice and handling of skins is discussed in detail in this book. The reader will learn everything that is involved in the design process—the research, creative, and merchandising planning process that can inspire a designer to create a successful line. The reader will be instructed about how to organize and plan a collection. The process of designing, editing, and merchandising a line, as well as presenting a line to clients, colleagues, or employers, using theme and style boards, will be explained. Highlighted in this book are actual theme and style boards used by major leather manufacturers. Also discussed is how to complete and use a design/spec sheet. Again, a compilation of design/spec sheets used by actual manufacturers is illustrated in this book.

The reader will be instructed about the techniques that are involved in constructing leather garments, with a focus on the technique that is commonly used in the leather apparel industry. All of the step-by-step instructions for constructing leather garments were photographed in an actual leather garment factory. The sewing guide demonstrates the construction of three different garments: a shirt, a pair of pants, and a jacket. By learning the techniques used to create these garments, the reader will be able to construct practically any leather garment.

Frank Rutland, an industry expert who was the former Director of the Leather Industries Research Laboratory, as well as the Technical Director of the Leather Industries of America, provided most of the information presented in the chapter on leather defects. This chapter thoroughly describes many of the most common leather defects. In addition, practical tips are provided about some of these problems.

The care and cleaning of leather skins and garments also is covered in this book. A list of recommended dry cleaners and leather care products is also provided.

Finally, this book includes a calendar of leather and fabric apparel industry events, a list of leather publications, organizations, and schools, and a helpful resource directory.

—Francesca Sterlacci, February 18, 1996

Acknowledgments

Many people have assisted in the preparation of this book, but the person who helped me most was my wonderful husband, Jeff Purvin. Jeff's patience, understanding, support, guidance, and love made this book possible. His countless hours of editing and advice were invaluable. I could not have done it without him, thus, I dedicated this book to him and to our son, Colton.

I also would like to thank the following people:

- Frank Rutland of the Leather Industries Research Laboratory at The University of Cincinnati for his significant assistance with the Leather Defects chapter
- Joan Glace for her photography in the sewing and historical sections of this book
- Jeanette Nostra and Carl Katz of GIII for writing the foreword to this book, contributing examples of design/spec sheets, and providing a jacket as a sewing example
- Barry Bornstein, Mitch Poctar, and Michael Zeidner at Vericci for providing a pair of pants as a sewing example and for helping me connect with the Marcelle leather apparel factory
- Marcelo Fogel and Juan Peguero at the Marcelle leather apparel factory for allowing me to photograph the step-by-step construction of a pair of pants and a shirt
- Pia and Terry at the Monkeyheads leather apparel factory for allowing me to photograph the step-by-step construction of a shirt
- Gina Madera, Ruby Ferrone, and Caezar Arreaga at Siena for too many contributions to enumerate
- Robert Pallateri at Siena Studio and Alicia Herrera at Siena for providing theme boards and sketches
- Alfred Satay at Bettina for allowing me to take photographs in the factory

- Lenore Benson, Edith Loss, and Dora Roberts at The Fashion Group International for their help while researching all of those wonderful leather clothes at The Fashion Group Archive
- Richard Martin and Dennita Sewell at The Metropolitan Museum of Art for allowing me to spend hours researching leather garments at the Costume Institute
- Ellen Shanley and Irving Solero at The Museum at the Fashion Institute of Technology for the leather coat photograph from the 1930s
- Professors at the Fashion Institute of Technology
  —Debbi Gioello for introducing me to my publisher
  —Linda Tain for her contributions to The Design Process chapter
  —Glenda Pike for her contributions to the chapter on Ultrasuede®
- Lili Kasdan, Chris Scardino, Richard Harrow, and Tom Sullivan of the Leather Apparel Association for answering innumerable questions
- Charles Meyers of the Leather Industries of America for answering many questions about the leather apparel industry
- Mitch Alfus of Libra Leather for his leather skins for the cover of this book, as well as the photograph of his father's kidskin coat
- Alfredo Motta at The Motta Alfredo tannery in Milan, Italy, for his help in describing the tanning process and for allowing me to photograph the process at the tannery
- Michele Filodemo, Felicina Simbolo, and Raffaele Gucci at the Santa Lucia tannery in Solofra, Italy, for permitting me to take photographs of the tannery
- Elva Shkreli and Steven Cutting for their help in the research process
- The Juki Sewing Machine Company for their photographs of leather sewing machines
- Andre Croteau for his illustrations and Piyawat Pattanapuckdee for his book cover illustration
- Michael Holzberg at Excelled Sheepskin for introducing me to Korea Merchandise Testing & Research Institute
- Korea Merchandise Testing & Research Institute for providing me with a leather test report

- Jeff Clyman and Frank Marchese at Avirex for contributing a photograph of an A-2 bomber
- David Dillman—who is still my inspiration

I would also like to thank the following reviewers:

Elaine Yingling
Bauder College
Arlington, TX

Dr. Catherine Boyd
Mississippi State University
Mississippi State, MS

Mary Rupert
Stephens College
Columbia, MO

Chapter

Leather's Beginnings

The Real Beginning: Food

Cro-Magnon man, the first prehistoric human, lived about 50,000 years ago in cooperative societies called tribes.

Obtaining food was a daily concern for members of Cro-Magnon tribes. Food spoiled quickly. Fruit and vegetable pickings were depleted around camps within weeks of setting up. Tribe members sometimes traveled for weeks, many miles each day, looking for food but often returning with nothing.

Winter for our ancestors was probably no colder than fifty degrees Fahrenheit. They could not survive in colder climates due to the lack of appropriate clothing. Yet, even during these relatively mild winters, all of the deciduous fruit- and vegetable-bearing trees and bushes lost their leaves in the fall. The only way our ancestors could survive winter was to store enough food each fall. This meant learning how to preserve food—by preserving their food, they could survive winter.

The tribes who survived used a number of methods to preserve their food. They learned that meats and fish smoked over a campfire tended to last longer and tasted good as well. They also learned that salt and air drying meats and fish in the sun were methods of food preservation. Most of these methods involved changing the nature of living tissue, making the food a poor environment in which bacteria

1

could live and multiply. Food spoilage is almost always due to bacteria. In the "right" environment, bacteria can thrive, however, the right environment requires a particular range of temperatures, environmental acidity, and, most important, water.

When early man learned how to preserve food, one of the most important keys to survival on earth was learned.

The Need for Clothes

Once our earliest relatives learned to preserve food, more survived. As a result, they could multiply more quickly. As overpopulation increased, food became more scarce and tribes began to migrate, moving south to warmer climates. In the northern hemisphere, the tribes that ended up dominating the entire world moved to the less hospitable, but relatively unpopulated, north.

Clothes Must Be Soft

Moving north created a problem, however. How could the men and women in these tribes keep themselves warm in the cold, often frigid, climates of the north? They could have worn furs or animal skins, but dried-out animal skins are very hard. The key to making animal skins into clothing was learning to make them *soft*. Although salting, drying, or boiling skins in bark can preserve them, these methods do not make them soft.

The tribe that first invented warm clothing, and also tanning, might have accidentally invented it. Tribe members might have been trying to use pieces of dried, hard-as-board animal skin as primitive food plates. Dried skin made a suitable plate, as long as it did not come into contact with large amounts of oil or fat, but the tribe might have noticed that after using its new plates to serve a few greasy meat dinners, the plates started to soften.

Over time, after much trial and error, a member of some ancient tribe[1] may have accidentally created the first truly tanned, preserved skin by drying it, boiling it with tree bark, then rubbing it with fresh animal fat, bending and working it until it became completely soft.

---

[1] Possibly a Cro-Magnon ancestor, maybe even an older ancestor, e.g., a Neanderthal.

This early tanner eventually discovered that since water and fat do not mix, the soft, slightly greasy skin was also waterproof.

Our earliest ancestors simply draped themselves with preserved skins, probably using crude ropes to tie the skins around their waists or heads. However, more recent ancestors used bone tools to sew their skins together to make clothing.

No one knows how tanning was first discovered. But it could be argued that, along with the preservation of food, the science of tanning, that is, preserving and softening animal skins, was one of the most important inventions in human history.

Leather Through the Ages

Cro-Magnon man first moved into Europe about 40,000 years ago. Archaeologists have evidence that these ancient peoples wore carefully designed, tailored clothing. However because our early ancestors could not write and because the ravages of time destroyed much of what they wore, the earliest available written records must be relied on in tracing leather's contribution to history.

THE MIDDLE EAST

In Mesopotamia, somewhere between the fifth and third millenniums B.C. the Sumerians used animal skins to create ladies' dresses.

In Egypt, leather artifacts were found in tombs built as early as 3000 B.C., evidence that the pharaohs wore leather sandals.

A loincloth of gazelle skin, worn by a woman in ancient Egypt during the Eighteenth Dynasty, 1580-1350 B.C. is almost perfectly preserved today (Figure 1–1).

The Old Testament makes numerous references to leather, crediting the Hebrews with the oak bark tanning process.

The trading of leather items throughout the Mediterranean was done by the Phoenicians of Babylon, who were great seafarers. A certain red dye is still known today as Phoenician Red.

THE FAR EAST

The ancient Chinese worked with leather to create elaborately decorated boxes, screens, and chests.

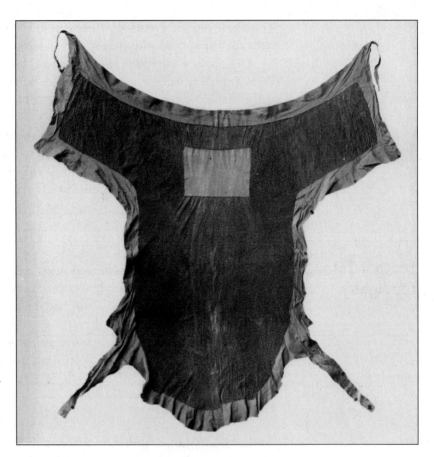

EUROPE

A tannery was uncovered in the ruins of Pompeii in Italy, providing some evidence that the Romans made leather footwear, clothing, and ornaments.

The Etruscans, who lived between 750 and 500 B.C., handed down their leatherworking skills to the Romans. The Roman Empire had a tanner's guild. Soldiers used leather for shields, breast plates, and sandals. While the Roman armies were fighting the nomadic Teutonic tribes in the cold north of Europe, they discovered that these tribes wore whole garments of leather. The soldiers came back to Rome wearing leather trousers called **braccae.**

In Spain, during the eighth century when the Moors ruled, a tanning process was created which produced the famous Cordovan

Leather, also called Spanish Leather. This leather featured a softly tanned goatskin, dyed in numerous colors and often perfumed. This type of leather was popular throughout Europe.

By the fifteenth century, many homes contained large quantities of finely detailed Spanish Leather, which was used in wall hangings, upholstery, book covers, vests, and jackets. Some of these objects were handpainted, carved, inlaid, or stamped in silver or gold.

Solofra, Italy, has an interesting history. Solofra is well known today for its many excellent tanneries. Yet the town was not originally famous for leather making. In the 1400s, it was famous for making gold leaf. Solofra was one of the centers of gold leaf manufacturing in Italy. Many of Italy's architects decorated their buildings with a thin veneer of gold leaf. Similarly, gold leaf was used by many artisans in picture frames, furniture, and other decorative objects.

To produce gold leaf, artisans pounded large ingots of gold into extremely thin sheets using large hammers. These artisans learned, after much trial and error, that gold is easier to form into gold leaf when it is hammered on a heavy leather pad. But because each pad took such a pounding over the course of a year, the artisans had to replace them quite frequently, importing the leather from faraway places at great expense.

To save money, many of these gold leaf makers started to tan their own leather to make the pounding pads, creating sideline businesses to sell leather saddles, whips, and boots.

When the architectural sensibilities of Italy and Europe moved away from the frequent use of gold leaf, many of the families of craftsmen whose livelihoods depended upon gold leaf had to find another business to support themselves. Many of them turned to tanning on a full-time basis. Today, gold leaf is not made in Solofra, yet it is the home of more than 200 tanners.

In sixteenth-century England, a typical Englishman wore a soft leather tunic. We know Englishmen drank their beer out of mugs that were made of leather.

The designer of the English doublet in Figure 1–2 used perforations to create a pattern. The designer of the seventeenth-century jerkin in Figure 1–3 added detachable sleeves and a chamois collar, which was bonded to wool.

In seventeenth-century France, the French nobility wore the leather gauntlet glove. However, the tanning process left a disagreeable odor on the gloves, so the French bathed the gloves in perfume.

FIGURE 1–2

An English doublet made of leather. (Courtesy of The Metropolitan Museum of Art, New York)

FIGURE 1–3

A seventeenth century English jerkin with detachable sleeves. (Courtesy of The Metropolitan Museum of Art, New York)

Since the French tanneries were all located in the south, the manufacturers of the perfumes would travel there to sell their products, and later they permanently established their industry in the south. Although the tanneries have long since moved, the perfume industry is still concentrated in Grasse, which is in the south of France.

SOUTH AMERICA

While Europe advanced in the art of leather tanning and design, the Aztec, Mayan, and Incan civilizations also advanced in their use of leather, making clothing out of the skins of local animals such as buck, buffalo, and deer.

NORTH AMERICA

When the first settlers came to the New World, they brought their own methods of tanning. From the American Indians, they learned a technique called **oil tanning**. The American Indians made tepees out of leather, decorated their leather clothes and moccasins with beads, feathers, porcupine quills, and bones, and sometimes painted scenes on leather to depict a famous battle.

American Indian tanning skills were quite advanced. The garment in Figure 1–4 shows the sophistication of American Indian tanning knowledge. Note that the dress is heavily beaded and fringed. But most noteworthy is that it is white, a particularly difficult color to produce in a tanned garment.

Tanneries appeared throughout the early American colonies by the late seventeenth century. Borrowing from the Indians, the early settlers of the American West wore leather-fringed buckskin jackets, vests, chaps, boots, and gauntlet gloves. Sometimes their hats were made of leather or were leather-trimmed.

During the nineteenth century, amidst the Industrial Revolution, an American chemist, Augustus Schultz, invented a newer and faster method of tanning using chromium salts. Instead of taking weeks or months to tan a skin, this new method of tanning took only hours. In both America and Europe, engineers invented special machines to increase tanning productivity. In 1809, a leather-splitting machine was patented that could split leather to any desired thickness.

FIGURE 1–4

An early 1800s white deerskin dress. (Courtesy of The Metropolitan Museum of Art, New York)

Figure 1–5 depicts a typical fringed cowskin men's coat, vest, and pants, made in New England, circa 1835.

The corset was popular from 1820 to 1930. Drawing inspiration from the leather armor worn in the eleventh century, clothing manufacturers realized that leather was a perfect material for use in the corset, as shown in the French corset in Figure 1–6.

THE 1900s. In the early 1900s, upon the advent of the open automobile, rich men wore long motoring coats made of leather to protect them from the elements. They also wore leather trench coats fashioned after the British military officer's coat (Figure 1–7).

FIGURE 1–5

*A men's fringed and embroidered
coat and vest (circa 1835).
(Courtesy of The Metropolitan
Museum of Art, New York)*

FIGURE 1–6

*French corset made of leather
(circa 1875). (Courtesy of
The Metropolitan Museum
of Art, New York)*

THE 1920s. During the 1920s, women's leather and suede sportswear began to appear, both in Europe and the United States.

Also during the 1920s and 1930s, interior designers such as Le Corbusier and Marcel Breuer integrated cowhides with their polished steel furniture during the Bauhaus period.

FIGURE 1–7

A 1930s men's distressed leather coat from France. (Courtesy of The Museum at the Fashion Institute of Technology)

FIGURE 1–8

Goat suede suit designed by Paquin (1930). (Courtesy of The Metropolitan Museum of Art, New York)

THE 1930s.   In France, in 1930, the designer Paquin created a suit using goat suede and wool (Figure 1–8).

In a 1938 issue of *Vogue*, an advertisement can be found for a suede bonnet, blouse, and skirt (Figure 1–9).

THE 1940s.   During the 1940s and 1950s, shades of tan, rust, and brown were predominant in suede for both men and women.

One of the most popular jacket styles in the 1940s was the aviator jacket (Figure 1–10). Even die-hard army commanders like General Patton wore them during WWII. The look of an aviator jacket is still quite distinctive today, and it continues to create a unique image for the wearer.

The quality of leather during the 1940s and 1950s was not particularly high. It tended to be quite stiff and came in just a few colors, mostly black, brown, and off-white.

FIGURE 1–9

A 1938 suede bonnet, blouse, and skirt

THE 1950s. Bonnie Cashin was the first American designer to create fashions extensively in leather and suede. (See Figure 1–11.)

In the late 1950s and early 1960s, on the eve of leather design's heyday, designers began experimenting with new colors in leather. (See the interesting rust-colored Hermes coatdress in Figure 1–12.)

The Albert Alfus coat, depicted in Figure 1–13, was originally offered for sale in sixteen different colors, including electric blue, pumpkin, avocado, and charcoal.

THE 1960s. In 1960, leather design came into its own, enjoying tremendous worldwide popularity.

Bonnie Cashin created many leather and suede garments, in combination with fabric and knit, as well as leather and suede ensembles. (See Figure 1–14.) She was at the vanguard of leather design. In Figure 1–15, note the Bonnie Cashin 1965 calf suede mini-dress with starburst appliqué.

Ornamented leather garments were fashionable, as evidenced by Nina Ricci's couture black leather floor-length evening coat with gold embroidery (Figure 1–16).

FIGURE 1–11

A 1953 Bonnie Cashin off-white cabretta leather coat. (Courtesy of The Metropolitan Museum of Art, New York)

FIGURE 1–12

A 1957 Hermes rust cowsplit coatdress. (Courtesy of The Metropolitan Museum of Art, New York)

FIGURE 1–13

A late 1950s Albert Alfus leather coat with fur trim

An abundance of leather clothing flooded the market in 1968 during the hippie movement.

Probably the most popular coat during the late 1960s was the embroidered goatskin jacket by Mallory (Figure 1–17).

As small boutiques cropped up and many new designers sold their clothes to these shops, leather clothing design prospered. Hand work such as fringing, beading, braiding, lacing, and painting

FIGURE 1–14

Bonnie Cashin suede ensemble.
(Courtesy of The Fashion
International Archives)

FIGURE 1–15

A Bonnie Cashin calf suede mini-dress (1965).
(Courtesy of the Metropolitan Museum
of Art Costume Institute)

FIGURE 1–16

Nina Ricci evening coat (1964). (Courtesy of The Fashion Group International Archives)

FIGURE 1–17

Embroidered goatskin jackets by Mallory (1968). Howell Conant, Life Magazine, *Time Inc.*

became especially popular. Figure 1–18 shows a wild 1968 purple cow suede fringed vest and chaps with a coordinated orange knit jumpsuit. Figure 1–19 shows a 1969 cow suede wrap skirt, replete with hand stitching, braiding, and painting.

Rudi Gernreich adopted a jungle theme with his fun 1966 calfskin suits, which featured cheetah, tiger, and giraffe prints stenciled on haired calfskin (Figure 1–20).

Patchwork leather garments also were popular, utilizing scraps of skins, which lowered the price of the garment and created the hippie "craftsy" look.

Designers such as Adolfo, however, created patchwork leather garments for the more sophisticated customer (Figure 1–21).

Figure 1–22 shows a Yves St. Laurent tailored black leather suit.

FIGURE 1–18

*A 1968 vest
and chaps.
(Courtesy of The
Metropolitan
Museum of Art,
New York)*

FIGURE 1–19

A 1969 wrap skirt in cow suede. (Courtesy of The Metropolitan Museum of Art, New York)

FIGURE 1–20

Rudi Gernreich's suits with animal prints (1966). Howell Conant, Life Magazine, Time Inc.

FIGURE 1–21

*Adolfo suede patchwork
skirt (1970). (Courtesy of
The Fashion Group
International Archives)*

FIGURE 1–22

*Yves St. Laurent black
leather suit (1967)*

THE 1970s.   The 1970s saw a return to the more sophisticated leather garment. Figure 1–23 features a sophisticated Anne Klein black leather fitted jacket.

Bonnie Cashin continued her passion for combining leather and knit with her 1973 big handkerchief calf suede skirt and knit midriff top (Figure 1–24).

Again, Bonnie Cashin comes through with a suede-and-fabric combination in 1973 alpaca wool coat with attached calf suede handbag and matching pants (Figure 1–25).

By 1978, Claude Montana was quickly establishing himself as the king of women's leather apparel design. His highly designed pieces were luxurious and generously cut, as pictured in this long red lamb leather coat (Figure 1–26).

FIGURE 1–23

Anne Klein black leather jacket (1970). (Courtesy of The Fashion Group International Archives)

FIGURE 1–24

Bonnie Cashin suede
handkerchief skirt and top
(1973). (Courtesy of The
Metropolitan Museum of
Art, New York)

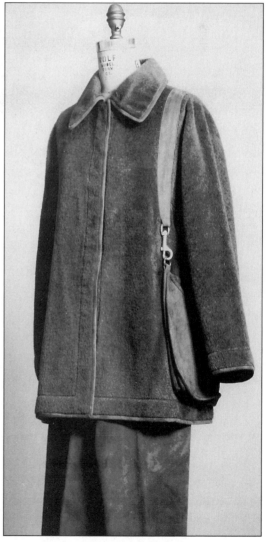

FIGURE 1–25

Bonnie Cashin suede
handbag jacket (1973).
(Courtesy of The
Metropolitan Museum
of Art, New York)

FIGURE 1–26

*Claude Montana
leather coat (1978).
(Courtesy of The
Fashion Group
International
Archives)*

THE 1980s.   By the 1980s, leather and suede continued to be a
luxury item. Designers used it as they would fabric. Skin size was no
longer a limitation because larger pig suede skins had become
increasingly available and designers who wanted to use smaller
lamb and goat suede skins become more adept at utilizing cut lines
in a creative way.

The French, English, and Italian designers led the way by
designing and inventing some of the most creative and saleable
leather clothing. Giorgio Armani, Claude Montana, Azzedine Alaia,

Anne Marie Baretta, Emanuel Ungaro, and Vivienne Westwood were the leaders. There seemed to be no limitations. Anything that could be done in cloth could be done in leather. The various weights and choices of skins that were being developed by tanneries and the vast assortment of colors, embossings, and prints made for a designer's dream. Leather and suede became a design material that signified wealth and taste, thereby solidifying its place in the designer market. (See Figures 1–27 through 1–34.)

American designers also were working in the medium during the 1980s. Designers such as Lisandro Sarasola, North Beach Leathers, Francesca Sterlacci, Adrienne Landau, Alicia Herrera, and Michael Kors worked mostly in leather.

FIGURE 1–27

Giorgio Armani diagonal patch leather top and pants (1980). (Courtesy of The Fashion Group International Archives)

FIGURE 1–28
Azzedine Alaia leather fitted suit (1984). (Courtesy of the Fashion Group International Archives)

FIGURE 1–29
Claude Montana jacket and dress (1980). (Courtesy of The Fashion Group International Archives)

FIGURE 1–32
Claude Montana
leather embroidered
coats (1987).
(Courtesy of The
Fashion Group
International
Archives)

FIGURE 1–33
Ungaro leather
ensemble (1988).
(Courtesy of The
Fashion Group
International
Archives)

FIGURE 1–34

Vivienne Westwood leather pouf dress (1988). (Courtesy of The Fashion Group International Archives)

THE 1990s.   Novelty skins were becoming popular as tanneries in Italy and France competed with each other to create unique looks.

Tanneries around the world began to copy the rich, luxe hand of the finest lamb leathers and suedes in less expensive animals such as pig and cow.

Leading designers such as Givenchy, Christian Lacroix, and Gianni Versace continued to work leather into their collections, even at the couture level (Figures 1–35 through 1–37).

FIGURE 1–35

*Gianni Versace couture
leather studded bustier
(1992). (Courtesy of The
Fashion Group
International Archives)*

FIGURE 1–36

Christian Lacroix couture leather jacket with snake trim (1992). (Courtesy of The Fashion Group International Archives)

FIGURE 1–37

Givenchy couture suede patchwork suit (1992). (Courtesy of The Fashion Group International Archives)

Designers such as Claude Montana, Christian Dior, Gucci, Mario Valentino, Hermes, Azzedine Alaia, Gianni Versace, and Fendi continued their spectacular work as more designers, such as Karl Lagerfeld, joined the bandwagon. (See Figures 1–38 through 1–47).

FIGURE 1–38

Gucci leather ensemble (1991).

(Courtesy of The Fashion Group International Archives)

FIGURE 1–39

Mario Valentino fringed suede suit (1991).

(Courtesy of The Fashion Group International Archives)

FIGURE 1–40

Karl Lagerfeld leather skirt (1992).
(Courtesy of The Fashion Group
International Archives)

FIGURE 1–41

Claude Montana suede batwing jacket
(1994). (Courtesy of The Fashion Group
International Archives)

FIGURE 1–42

Azzedine Alaia blue suede ensemble (1993). (Courtesy of The Fashion Group International Archives)

FIGURE 1–43

Claude Montana leather swing coat (1990). (Courtesy of The Fashion Group International Archives)

FIGURE 1–44

*Gucci brown suede dress (1993).
(Courtesy of The Fashion Group
International Archives)*

FIGURE 1–45

*Gianni Versace perforated leather jacket
and skirt (1994). (Courtesy of The
Fashion Group International Archives)*

FIGURE 1–46
Christian Dior leather jacket (1995).
(Courtesy of The Fashion Group
International Archives)

FIGURE 1–47
Fendi metallic leather coat (1995).
(Courtesy of The Fashion Group
International Archives)

Several young American designers such as Zang Toi, Byron Lars, Isaac Mizrahi, and Anna Sui are famous for adding whimsy to their designs. (See Figures 1–48 through 1–50.)

FIGURE 1–48

Zang Toi patchwork leather coat (1992).
(Courtesy of The Fashion Group
International Archives)

FIGURE 1–49

Byron Lars leather aviator jacket (1992).
(Courtesy of The Fashion Group
International Archives)

FIGURE 1–50
*Isaac Mizrahi leather
pocketbook jacket (1992).
(Courtesy of The
Fashion Group
International Archives)*

Many of the top American designers, such as Ralph Lauren (Figure 1–51), Anne Klein, Calvin Klein, Geoffrey Beene, Norma Kamali, Donna Karan, and Bill Blass, almost routinely include leather in their collections.

FIGURE 1–51

Ralph Lauren leather jacket with Persian lamb trim (1993). (Courtesy of The Fashion Group International Archives)

Leather apparel is a $3 billion industry in the United States. The industry is comprised of many companies that manufacture leather garments worldwide. These companies manufacture for all levels of the marketplace, from the designer to budget category.

The history of leather spans an unbelievable length of time, from the earliest tanner to today's sophisticated fashion connoisseur. Although leather tanning had its roots in early human's survival, it has since become a respected and beautiful art form.

The Tanning Process

What Tanning Does

Leather is animal skin that has been **tanned**. Tanning does two things to animal skin.

1. It preserves animal skin so that it will not decompose.
2. It adds fat to the hide to make it soft.

Leather is made by tanneries. A **tannery** is a factory that buys raw skins, makes the skins into leather, colors the leather, and sells it to garment manufacturers.

The Major Leather Manufacturing Steps

Tanned leather is produced in three distinct stages.

First, a tannery must place an order for hides. It can place an order for a particular type or quality of leather requested by an individual garment manufacturer and/or it can place an order anticipating future demand for many different garment manufacturers.

Second, a slaughterhouse (or, as it is often more delicately termed, an **abattoir**) must kill an animal and process its hide properly for transport to a tannery. Animals that have been poorly killed or processed will produce poor leather.

The third major stage in leather making is the tanning process itself.

STAGE 1: HOW TANNERIES PURCHASE QUALITY SKINS

To make leather, tanneries must first purchase skins from abattoirs. The purchasing process is one of the most important steps in leather making. Even the best tanneries cannot make quality leather out of poor-quality raw skins.

A quality tannery goes through a series of steps when purchasing leather. It should be noted that tanneries may vary considerably in their raw skin purchasing skills.

SELECTING THE TYPE OF SKIN TO PURCHASE. The skins from different animals produce profoundly different leathers. For example, pigs have numerous, thick-shafted hair follicles. As a result, pig leather is covered with many visible dots.

Cowskin is tougher than lambskin because it is denser and thicker. In addition, because cowskin is thicker, it can be split into two skins, called **splits**, doubling its yield. Pigskin can also be split. For the end user, the top grain side of a split hide is not cheaper to purchase; only the inside of the split is cheaper.

Lambskin is the most widely used skin in clothing design because it has an extremely soft feel when tanned properly. However, because lambs are small, their yield per skin is low, resulting in a higher cost per garment. Goat leather can be softer than lamb, but because its yield is even lower per skin, it is more expensive than lamb.

Leather can be made from just about any animal or fish skin. Some common leather sources include:

- lamb
- salmon
- goat
- peccary
- pig
- python
- shark
- deer
- horse
- caiman crocodile
- elk
- water buffalo
- cow

DECIDING WHERE TO OBTAIN THE SKIN. Most good tanneries have a list of favored sources for almost any type of skin. They have created this list based on years of experience. However, when selecting suppliers, tanneries must be mindful of many geographical factors.

The animal skins used in leather making come from all over the world. The quality of skins varies significantly depending on their source, even among the same animals.

The quality of lambskin, one of the most prized skins in leather making, varies enormously depending on its country of origin. Most quality tanneries favor lambskin that comes from New Zealand or England (called **English domestic**). However, good-quality lambskins also come from Italy, Iran, Iraq, Spain, India, Pakistan, Australia, and the United States.

The country of origin is not always a sufficient determinant of skin quality, which may vary within a country's borders, depending on the severity of its regional climate, differences in regional soil quality (which affects the quality of the grass the animals eat), and the care provided by various ranchers.

Some skins are so rare that they can come from a few sources, for example, kangaroo from Australia, python from Africa, and so on.

Other specialty skins might come from the following countries:

- Norway (elk)
- Brazil (peccary)
- Denmark (horse)
- United States (salmon)
- Ethiopia (water buffalo)
- Japan (crocodile)

DECIDING WHEN TO BUY THE SKIN. The better tanneries know exactly when to purchase skins from a particular location. Even when they do not have in-house orders from garment manufacturers for a particular type of leather, tanneries might purchase the leather anyway, storing it for later use because they know there is a specific time to purchase the required skins.

Timing is especially critical when purchasing young animal skins, for example, lamb (baby sheep) and calf (baby cows). Since most animals produce their young during a specific period, usually in the spring, tanneries need to know exactly when to put in their orders for specific hides. Naturally, this timing will vary by six months between countries south of the equator, where spring starts in October, and countries north of the equator, where spring starts in April.

STAGE 2: HOW ABATTOIRS PROCESS SKINS

KILLING THE ANIMAL. One of the first steps in creating leather unfortunately involves the death of an animal. Most animal skins used in leather making come from abattoirs. These sources invariably use the rest of the animal for food.

The abattoirs in developed countries use humane methods to kill the animals, for example, by applying an electrically charged probe to the head of the animal. Most animals are only stunned by the probe, not killed. Once stunned, the animal is often hung by its hind legs. The actual slaughter is completed by bleeding the animal to death by cutting its key arteries.

Tanneries prefer killing methods that do not reduce skin yield. If an animal is agitated by fear or has had significant physical exercise prior to being stunned and bled, it cannot be fully bled, leaving random pools of blood in the flesh and skin. This produces bruise marks on the skin and increases the speed at which the skin will decompose. The bruise marks or **cockles**, veins that appear in irregular patterns on raw skin, permanently lower the quality of the skin. The bruises make it impossible for tanneries to color the skin uniformly.

Although most abattoirs go out of their way to assure that their animals are calm before slaughter, sometimes the quality of the kill cannot be controlled. For example, almost all of the 400,000 deerskins exported from the United States are shot by rifle or arrow. These skins are usually blemished by bullet holes, drag marks, and poor skinning techniques, often initiated by inexperienced hunters.

From a garment maker's perspective, it is important to note that any blemishes, bruises, or other seemingly minor imperfections in a raw hide will be visually accentuated by the tanning process.

FLAYING THE SKIN. **Flaying** the skin means removing it from an animal carcass by hand and/or machine. First, the butcher (or hunter) makes cuts all around the animal with a sharp knife. Simultaneously pulling the skin and using the knife to slice the connective tissue removes the animal's skin. Sometimes, however, the knife cuts the skin itself instead of its underlying tissue.

Sophisticated butchers connect special skinning machines to the ends of cut skin which then pull the skin off the animal. Skinning machines produce much cleaner, less damaged skins than manual flaying methods.

Generally, hoofed animals are cut straight up and down on their bellies, and the skin is pulled around the (already removed) legs. This protects the valuable skin on the back of the animal from cuts. The exact opposite process is used for saurians (crocodiles and lizards), whose bellies are the most important leather sources. These animals are first cut along their back, then skinned toward their front.

After flaying, skins must be quickly washed with cool water to slow the rotting process.

CURING THE SKIN. **Curing** is a process that protects animal skins from rotting. Newly flayed skins should be cured within six hours to prevent rotting. At this early stage in the skin production process, only short-term preservation methods are necessary. Generally, abattoirs try to complete within a few weeks all of the steps leading to the shipment of skins to tanneries.

Rotting, or putrefaction, of the skin is caused by bacteria on the skin. This bacteria produces enzymes that can liquefy the surface of animal hides. These liquefied portions of hide are absorbed by the bacteria as food. The rotted portions of an animal hide produce permanent blemishes, which significantly reduce its value to garment makers.

There are three main methods of curing skins—refrigeration, drying, and chemical treatment.

REFRIGERATION. Many abattoirs have freezer or refrigeration facilities. An uncured, refrigerated animal skin can be stored about two weeks without damage. Frozen skins can be safely kept for longer periods of time; however, freezing sometimes damages the skin if ice crystals form within the skin fiber.

DRYING. Most bacteria need water to survive, thus by drying animal skins thoroughly, most bacteria cannot feed normally. When this occurs over a prolonged period of time, some bacteria die while other bacteria revert to a dormant spore form. Bacterial spores, however, can quickly become hungry bacteria when skins are rehydrated. For effective drying, skins must contain no more than 10 to 14 percent moisture.

Usually, abattoirs dry skins by hanging them up to air dry, although some place their skins on the ground to sun dry. Since so many skins come from lesser-developed countries in hot, dry climates, air drying is relatively easy and effective. It is more difficult to dry skins in cooler, northern climates. This is a problem for the abattoirs and tanners in the upper northern or southern hemispheres of the world, because if skins are dried too slowly they can putrefy before their moisture content drops low enough to stop bacterial action.

CHEMICAL TREATMENT.   Even when water is present, rotting can be slowed or stopped by dissolving specific elements in the water, for example, salts, acids, alkalis, bactericides, and other toxic chemicals. The most commonly used elements are salts and acids.

Some abattoirs treat animal skins with special chemicals to prevent rotting by adding the chemicals to large, rotating drums filled with skins.

There are a number of chemical approaches to preserving animal skins. One common approach is to add chemicals that impart a mild acidity level of about 4.5 pH to the skins. This mildly acidic environment is lethal to most bacteria. Another less toxic approach involves immersing the skins in a solution of boric acid, a mild antiseptic. These preservation methods can last anywhere from a few days to a few weeks, until the abattoir finds the time to complete the unhairing and pickling processes.

Salting is the preferred method of preserving skins. To salt skins, abattoirs stack animal hides flesh side up, thoroughly covering each hide with coarse grain salt. The amount of salt used to cover the raw hides is generally 25 to 35 percent of the weight of the raw hides. The more sophisticated abattoirs immerse newly flayed skins in a brine solution (three percent of salt per gallon of water) for twelve hours, then stack the skins. Salting can preserve skins for months, or longer, if the skins are both salted and dried.

UNHAIRING THE SKIN.   Abattoirs must remove the hair from animal skins prior to transporting the skins to tanneries.

Some skins, such as lamb, have a high market value. When abattoirs want to sell the fur (for wool) they treat the skins with special chemicals so they can remove the fur by hand, without damaging it. First, the skins are immersed in a highly alkaline lime or lye bath to loosen the hair. Then the piled skins are sprayed (on their flesh sides) with an acid, usually sulfuric acid, or other chemicals. After one to two hours, the chemicals penetrate the skin, which allows abattoirs to remove the fur by hand, usually with a special defleshing knife.

When abattoirs do not wish to sell the fur, for example, cowhides, they throw the skins in a drum with sulfuric acid or other chemicals and rotate the drum until all of the fur is gone.

When most of the hair is removed, abattoirs wash and clean the animal skins thoroughly to remove lime and any remaining blood, dirt, fur, fat, and bacteria. Hunters often use vinegar to neutralize the lime in the skin, a process called **bating**.

PICKLING.   Before storage or transport to tanneries, hairless skins are invariable pickled, dried, or both. Most often they are shipped in a pickled state.

To **pickle** skins, abattoirs gently rotate the skins in drums with a mixture of water, salt, and sulfuric acid for approximately two hours. Although pickling stops bacterial activity cold, it will not prevent mold growth. Since mold attacks the basic structure of the skin, uneven dyeing and loss of gloss can occur when the skin is eventually tanned. To prevent mold, low concentrations of fungicides are added to the pickling solution.

After pickling, skins are piled into a waterproof container for bulk shipment to tanneries. Stacked lamb skins, after the pickling process, resemble a pile of thick, white, wet paper.

Pickled skins can be stored for several months, if kept relatively cool.

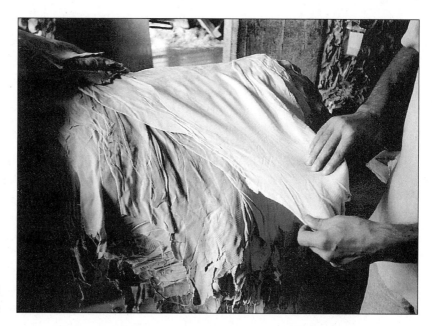

FIGURE 2–1

Pickled skins

CRUSTS. A dried raw animal skin is called a **crust**. As noted earlier, skins are dried into crusts by hanging them in the air in a carefully controlled environment. Many abattoirs ship skins, with or without pickling them, as crusts. Since crusts are rigid, they are susceptible to cracking or creasing when they are bent. As a result, they must be carefully tied up, or baled, before shipment to tanneries. Crusts are susceptible to insect infestation, so they are often treated with insecticides or poisons such as arsenic.

FINAL DEFLESHING. Although abattoirs remove most of the animal flesh from skins before they ship them to tanneries, a white, wispy residue of flesh appears on the inside of the skins. If the tannery does not scrape off all of the flesh before the tanning process, the tanned skins will have an uneven coloration due to poor, irregular penetration of color dyes.

To remove the remaining flesh on a newly purchased skin, a tannery will insert it into a machine that has rollers on the top and bottom. The machine's stationary sharp cutting blade is placed very close to the bottom roller. As the skin enters the machine through the two rollers, the blade scrapes the residue of flesh off of the skins.

STAGE 3: THE TANNING PROCESS

Most quality leather or suede garments are made from the skins of the lamb or goat. Sometimes, however, cowskin is more expensive than lambskin. Because of the popularity of the latter, this book will concentrate on the tanning process of those skins. Note though that a similar process is employed to tan the skins of other animals.

A tannery that specializes in lambskins usually received pickled raw skins from its suppliers. Occasionally, the tannery will receive skins as crusts. In the latter case, the tannery will soak the crusts in salt water until the skins are thoroughly wet. This brine solution helps open the pores of the skin for better penetration of tanning solutions.

There is no way to generalize the tanning process for all skins. Each skin is different and must be treated as such. The specific amount of chrome powder, basifying agent(s), fat liquor(s), waterproofing agents, softeners, and so on, added to skins during the tanning process varies significantly depending on the animal and the location from which it came. For example, New Zealand lambskin is tanned using different "recipes" than that of Australian lambskin or English domestic lambskin.

There really is only one limiting factor in tanning—the quality of the original raw skin itself. Tanning cannot make a poor-quality skin into an excellent skin. While tanneries can influence certain quality variables (i.e., adding more vegetable tannins to make skins drier or adding more fat liquors to make skins softer), they cannot make a skin any drier or softer than its original raw potential allows.

In the next few pages, many of the key steps in the tanning process will be summarized. However, different tanneries execute the tanning process in different ways. For example, a tannery that specialized in cheap leather for novelty clothing might skip some of the expensive labor-intensive procedures such as final defleshing (see the section on Final Defleshing). Also, many of the high-quality tanneries utilize expensive secret processes, while the cheaper tanneries try hard to avoid any extra steps to the tanning process.

Making "Wet Blues"

Making "wet blues" is really the most important step in the tanning process. In fact, this is the only step which is actually called tanning by the industry.

To produce **wet blues**, tanneries place fully defleshed, pickled animal skins into large rotating drums. (See Figure 2–2.) These drums, which often are made of wood and look like giant wooden barrels, can hold between 1,000 to 3,000 skins each. Tannery personnel rotate the skins in the drums for approximately eight hours, and add chromium sulfate powder plus other (often proprietary) ingredients.

When the skins emerge from drums, they are a light-colored blue (Figure 2–3). The tannery sets the newly tanned skins out for three days to allow the chrome solution to seep into the thickest parts of the skins. After the tanning occurs, tanneries usually wash the skins in water to eliminate the excess chromium salt.

Chrome is the key element in chromium sulfate. Chrome transforms the natural proteins in skins to inert substances that resist rotting. Skins that have been tanned with chrome never lose their tannage, even when soaked in water.

FIGURE 2–2

Tanning drum

FIGURE 2–3

Wet blues

ALTERNATE "TANNING" INGREDIENTS

In previous years, homes and tanneries used vegetable matter to tan skins. This process usually involved boiling tree bark and/or other vegetable matter until a "tea" filled with natural vegetable **tannin** was produced. In fact, the term "tanning" came from the original process of immersing raw skins in a tannin-containing solution. The most common vegetable sources for natural tannins include oak bark, hemlock bark, gambier, terra japonica, and various byproducts of the wood-processing industry.

RETANNING

Some tanneries insert additional steps between tanning and the next wet process or **neutralization**. In this step, the wet blues are processed with special ingredients designed to make the skins lighter, softer, harder, or whatever is desired by the tannery. For example, if the tannery wants to constrict the fibers of the skins to minimize skin pore size, it might add aluminum-containing powder to the retanning drums. Generally, tanneries put the skins designated for retanning into the same drums they plan to use for dyeing, and not the initial tanning drums.

STORING SKINS FOR LATER USE

Occasionally, a tannery might want to store the resultant, fully defleshed, wet blue skins for a time before processing them further. This would occur, for example, if the tannery had purchased more skins than it had open manufacturer orders.

To store already-tanned skins, tanneries dry them into crusts. To accomplish this, the tanneries first wring out the excess moisture by inserting skins into a large machine with two long rollers, called the **setting out machine**. (See Figure 2–4.) The wringing-out process is called **setting out** the skins.

Following the setting out process, the skins are hung and left to air dry for several days. Some tanners have very large drying machines that are 40 to 60 feet long. These tanneries hang their skins on a moving overhead conveyor belt to transport the hanging skins into and out of the dryer. When the skins exit the dryer, they are fully dried.

Crusts can be stored for years, even indefinitely, without deteriorating.

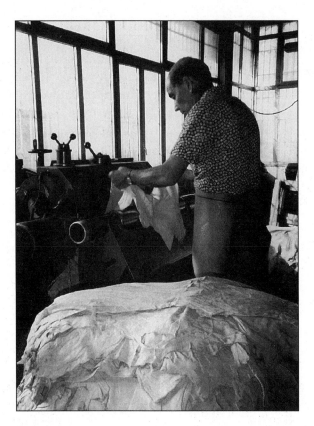

FIGURE 2–4

Setting out machine

Sorting and Selecting Skins

The sorting process can occur anytime during the pre- or post-tanning (wet blue) process. In fact, it usually occurs several times per skin. Even though most tanneries work hard to buy the best possible skins initially, they still spend a considerable amount of time evaluating and reevaluating the skins they already own.

First, a tannery sorts skins based on their physical qualities. During this procedure, trained tannery inspectors examine the crusts on tables. Different skins that come from the same type of animal may have different physical flaws, for example, one animal may have been severely cut by barbed wire during its lifetime, another may have been poorly flayed by an abattoir or inexperienced hunter, or an animal may have had cockles, or veins that show up in irregular patterns on the skin.

Second, the tannery decides which skins should be made into **suede** (where the *inside* of the skin will be worn on the outside of a garment) and which skins will be made into nappa (where the outside, formerly fur-bearing, side of the skin will be worn on the out-side of a garment). Tanneries make this determination by carefully examining both the inside and outside (also called the **grain side**) of the skins. In a fine tannery, 50 percent of its output might be nappa and 50 percent might be suede. Suede can be made with relatively lower-quality skins than nappa. Thus, although suede requires several more processing steps than nappa, it usually costs garment manufacturers less to purchase it.

Neutralizing

Wet blues, as discussed previously, are made from pickled skins, that is, skins that are treated with sulfuric acid. As a result, wet blues are quite acidic (2.0 to 3.0 pH). Before the skins can be predyed and dyed, they must be made more alkaline (about 5.0 pH). Tanneries add **basifying agents** to rotating drums containing wet blues to neutralize their acidity.

Preparations for Dyeing

Following the neutralization process, tanneries add other ingredients to newly tanned skins. The ingredients vary, depending on the type and quality of skins being processed and on the experience, tradition, and research and development (R&D) sophistication of each tannery.

A mandatory additive used in the tanning process is **fat liquor**. Fat liquor conditions (i.e., adds oils to) skins. In many ways, this is the most important additive, outside of chrome, because it returns the skin to its natural softness.

The very best skins will be processed with fat liquor and other ingredients to prepare them for becoming **aniline** skins, that is, very soft skins without any sprayed-on additives. Aniline skins are preprocessed so that later, during the dyeing process, dyes can penetrate the skins completely, from one side to the other. Aniline skins do not require sprayed-on, cover-up dyes to hide defects; they can be either nappa or suede.

The majority of skins have visible flaws, some minor, others quite visible. These skins must be further processed to become **semi-aniline** nappa. A semi-aniline skin is any skin that undergoes a surface treatment, which involves spraying skins with coats of dye or plastic film, which is designed to obscure flaws. (The pros and cons of aniline versus semi-aniline skins will be discussed later in this chapter.) There really is no suede counterpart to this grade.

The remaining crusts in a tannery's inventory will have flaws so severe they can be used only for hidden garment linings. Some of these leathers also may be printed with designs that will hide their defects.

Dyeing the Skins

The color of fine leather is one of its most important attributes.

To dye skins, tanneries place them into special dyeing drums (Figure 2–5), unlike tanning drums that are used to make wet blues. The tanneries add special dyes and several other (often proprietary) ingredients to the drums. The dyes usually are purchased from companies that specialize in selling tanning supplies.

Most tanneries add the dyes by hand to the drums. Some sophisticated tanneries use computer-controlled, automatic ingredient feeders to add various ingredients to the dye bath in the drums. These sophisticated systems add dyes and other chemicals based on the weight of the skins in the drums.

The skins are wet when they are removed from the drums (Figure 2–6) and are put on rolling pallets when they sit for a while to drain. Tanneries will then dry the skins using the setting out process, that is, putting the skins through giant rollers.

Some ultra-thin suedes are too delicate for roller machines, thus they are carefully vacuumed by placing the skins, several at a time, on a large flat surface; then a second vacuum machine descends on top of the skins, sucking the water out as it presses on their tops.

The skins are then air-dried, either by hanging out the skins to dry naturally or by moving them via a conveyer device through a heated, forced-ventilation drying tunnel (Figure 2–7).

Staking

Since the drying process slightly shrinks the skins, the **staking process** seeks to stretch them to their normal size without rewetting them.

FIGURE 2–5

Dyeing drums

FIGURE 2–6

Wet dyed skins

There are two main ways to stake leather—by putting it through giant rollers to flatten it or by hand.

For high-volume staking, most tanneries use high-volume staking machines (Figure 2–8), which work much like setting out machines, that is, they pull skins through two rollers and flatten

FIGURE 2–7

Air drying skins

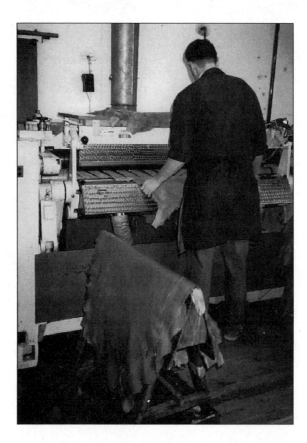

FIGURE 2–8

Staking (by machine)

them into slightly resilient (but mostly rigid) pancakes. At the end of this phase, the crust no longer has upturned edges.

Some tanneries stake their higher-quality, smaller skins the old-fashioned way, by hand. They might use any one of the various machines to assist in their objective, but the effort put into each skin involves highly skilled manual labor.

Most of the hand-staking operations involve machines of some sort. However, unlike the high-volume staking machines which literally roll over the entire skin at once, hand-staking machines only stake one small part of the skin's surface during each pass of the device.

A typical hand-staking machine has a large wheel, about the size of a narrow automobile tire, which rotates away from the machine's operator. Each wheel contains many dull blades, each running from left to right. The machine operator takes a skin and holds the two width-side edges of it with both hands and, while stretching the skin between two arms, presses the skin against the rotating wheel of the machine.

The above operation is repeated over and over again until all surfaces of the skin have been staked to the operator's satisfaction.

Obviously, this process costs significantly more than the high-volume method. Buy the better tanneries routinely hand stake their leathers, using different, highly specialized machines or wheel surfaces to produce a varied appearance and/or softness in their more expensive products.

For example, if a "better" tannery wanted to produce an aniline nappa leather with a particularly shiny surface, it might stake the leather using an old, one-of-a-kind "glazing" machine (Figure 2–9). These machines are often designed and created by the tanneries themselves.

A top-quality tannery in Italy features a custom-made machine that repeatedly rolls a small 5-inch roller over the skins, using extraordinarily heavy pressure (Figure 2–10). The machine's operator must continually move the skin, by hand, underneath the ever-rolling glass roller until the entire skin has been rolled. Because the whole process is done by hand, any area of the skin that needs an extra press from the glass roller can get it.

The glazing process results in a totally uniform, naturally shiny leather product, without the somewhat artificial look of sprayed-on shininess that results from the semi-aniline process.

FIGURE 2–9

Glazing machine

FIGURE 2–10

Glazing glass roller

Grading the Skins

Tanneries decide well before their skins are dyed whether the skin will be aniline or semi-aniline.

After staking, the potential aniline skins are separated from the other skins. They are graded as being either A, B, or C quality. Naturally, A quality aniline skins earn the tannery more money than B or C skins. The better tanneries produce 50 percent A, 30 percent B, and 20 percent C quality aniline skins. Garment makers should note, however, that these grades are based on the tannery's own judgment. The tannery's natural inclination will be to upgrade, not downgrade, a skin's quality. Some designers joke that tanneries seem to produce 95 percent A and 5 percent B quality skins on a consistent basis. The garment maker, when buying aniline skins, would be wise to visit tanneries to choose A quality skins.

A few years ago, a typical tannery sought to produce only aniline skins because it could sell them at a higher cost per skin then semi-aniline skins. In today's market, many manufacturers actively seek good semi-aniline skins, which may not look noticeably different from an aniline skin that has been processed with water-repellent chemicals during the tanning process.

Spray Treatments

Most skins that are purchased by even the best tanneries have serious enough physical defects to warrant spraying to the skins to hide surface flaws. As discussed earlier, any skin that undergoes any sort of surface treatment, whether it involves spraying on extra coats of dye, or merely a clear plastic film, is called a semi-aniline skin.

Semi-aniline skins are often less expensive than aniline skins. However, they usually do not have the soft feel and subtle coloration of aniline skins. On the other hand, since they are often protected by sprayed-on chemicals, they usually are more resistant to water and other spills than aniline skins.

Tanneries prepare semi-aniline skins by using two giant machines—a spraying machine and a drying machine. The skins are placed down flat onto wide conveyer belts, two to three skins wide. The belts move the skin into a spraying machine. The machine has four to six air pressure-controlled spray nozzles, each connected to a central hub located above the flat skins, which rotate at 50-60 rpm. As the skins pass below the rotating nozzles, the machine sprays dyes or other chemicals onto them (Figure 2–11).

FIGURE 2–11

Spraying skins

After the skins have been sprayed, they move immediately into a drying machine. The drying machine is always physically connected to the spraying machine. The drying machine uses steam heat and forced ventilation (fans) to dry the skins during the minute or so it takes the conveyer belts to move them through the machine.

The above two steps, spraying and drying, are usually repeated several times. The tanneries simplify this process by stringing together several pairs of sprayers and dryers, all fed by the same wide conveyer belt. Since these machines are quite large, a large string of perhaps five pairs of sprayers and dryers might extend in length to 130 to 150 feet. Normally, the number of sprayer/dryer pairs linked together ranges between three and five. A typical tannery, if there is such a thing, will amost always have at least two separate spraying lines.

The tanneries spray two different types of ingredients onto semi-aniline skins. First, several additional coats of dye might be sprayed on the skin to cover imperfections. Second, different films might be sprayed on the skins to produce specific qualities, depending on a customer's request, for example, to make the surface of a skin more glossy, or to waterproof a skin.

For high-quality semi-aniline skins (but not high enough quality to make them pure aniline), tanneries may try to limit their spray treatments to one coat of clear plastic film, either to waterproof or to create shine on the surface of the skin. These additives will conceal minor blemishes and discolorations on the skins.

There is always one unfortunate, but unavoidable, consequence of spraying skins, that is, they will lose some of their softness. A skin that is sprayed only once with a particularly light film or dye will always be noticeably harder to the touch than equal-quality, unsprayed skins.

In general, semi-aniline skins are rated lower than aniline skins made from equal-quality hides, however, many well-made semi-aniline skins can be breathtakingly beautiful and are virtually indistinguishable from aniline skins. They also can be just as expensive or more expensive than aniline skins. They may even be a better choice for garment design than aniline skins.

The Design Process

This chapter outlines the technique a designer might employ to create a collection for a leather apparel manufacturer. Naturally, one cannot *exactly* define how a designer should approach the creative process. Many of the great designers approach it quite differently. However, the approach described in this chapter is recommended because it is both thorough and effective.

Research and Inspiration

DEFINE THE CUSTOMER

Know your customer's profile, that is, his or her age and socioeconomic background, in order to design clothes that he or she can afford and will want to wear. For example, if your customer is young, design clothes that are trendy, fun, and affordable. Pay particular attention to the price of the skins you select for your design. Similarly, if you have an older "missy" customer, you may want to design a more conservative or classic garment, paying particular attention to interesting details. Skins would be chosen based on the price range of the clothes designed.

SHOP THE STORES

Market research is the best way to discover firsthand what the competition is doing as well as to learn what your customer is buying. It also gives the designer the opportunity to see what types of skins other designers are using, what silhouettes are being shown that season, and what the price points are.

ATTEND FORECAST AND TREND SHOWS

Most designers want to know what the fashion industry trend services will be predicting for the upcoming season. While there are no trend services exclusively for leather apparel, forecast services such as Here & There, Promostyl, and Pat Tunsky provide information that can be used by leather apparel manufacturers. These services predict color, fabric, silhouette, and trend information for a membership fee. Cotton Incorporated and DuPont are fiber companies that offer free trend and color information. (See the Resource Directory in Appendix C for more information about these services.)

ATTEND TRADE SHOWS

Numerous leather shows are held throughout the year. (See Appendix A for the section on the Leather Show Calendar of Events for details regarding the most popular of these events around the world.) The shows allow designers to stay abreast of the latest trends and advances in leather skin tanning and design. New treatments, colors, and skin textures are continually being introduced there. Leather designers also should keep up-to-date on textile trends by attending the top fabric shows, for example, Premier Vision in Paris (October and March) and the International Fashion Fabric Exhibition in New York (October and March).

MAKE TRAVEL PLANS DESIGNED TO CREATE INSPIRATION

Many manufacturers find traveling to Paris, Amsterdam, London, Milan, Florence, Munich, Dusseldorf, Montreal, Tokyo, Barcelona, and Brussels inspirational. They might photograph merchandise in store windows, sketch items they see, and/or purchase items they might wish to copy or interpret for their own collections. This way, management can see firsthand the new merchandise and trends.

READ MAGAZINES AND NEWSPAPERS

Designers should always read fashion magazines for color and trend directions. (See Appendix C, Resource Directory, for a list of the top leather magazines.) In addition to the specialized leather apparel magazines, designers should read all of the most important fashion magazines, both American and European, such as *Vogue, Harper's Bazaar, Elle, Marie Claire, L'Uomo, Collezioni,* and *Outerwear.* Designers also should regularly read trade papers, for example, *Women's Wear Daily* and the *Daily News Record* for up-to-the-minute information. If a designer is affiliated with a manufacturer that is a member of the Leather Industries of America or the Leather Apparel Association, then he or she also should be reading the newsletter produced by these trade organizations for current information. (See the section on Trade Organizations in Appendix B.)

ACTIVELY RESEARCH MUSEUMS AND LIBRARIES

Designers can gain inspiration from numerous sources, but one of the best ways is by studying what previous designers have done. Many museums throughout the world, such as the Metropolitan Museum of Art in New York, exhibit the costumes of a particular designer and/or of a certain period in history. These shows can have a surprisingly great influence on modern-day fashion trends. The Fashion Institute of Technology, also in New York, features wonderful exhibits and an extensive costume library, as does the Musée de la Mode in Paris. All of the above-mentioned institutions also have book and magazine costume libraries.

NOTE NON-FASHION EVENTS AND TRENDS

Designers should always be aware of all events occurring in the world. Current trends in music, movies, dance, theatre, and even local news can be potential sources of design inspiration. Some of the major fashion trends of the past have resulted from such influences.

For example, many designers have tied their collection to the musical trends of grunge and hip-hop. Sometimes, just people watching from a park bench or from a table at a sidewalk cafe can provide enough inspiration.

Organizing and Planning the Collection

Once the designer has accomplished the preceding steps, he or she should possess information to organize and plan a collection. By focusing on the fashion interests and economic means of the customer, the designer should be able to forecast what fashions must be created.

The designer, having properly researched his or her market, should know what skins will be important during the coming season. A color story should be established for the line, that is, two to six colors (per skin quality) should be selected that will best complement the line.

One of the best ways the designer can organize his or her thoughts and ideas is to create a theme board. Later, a style board should be created. These not only help the designer visualize the line, but also are extremely effective in helping present concepts to the manufacturer's sales staff and retail buyers.

The combination of a theme and style board can be very cost-effective, since they help the designer and manufacturer determine the viability of a line concept before the expensive process of sample making is initiated.

CREATE A THEME BOARD

A theme board is a visual presentation used by the designer to communicate the general concept or mood that will help sell a particular line to a target customer.

Most theme boards (also called concept boards or **mood boards**) consist of a collage of photographs, tear sheets, or photocopies from books or magazines, which are mounted on ¼" or ½" foam core board. Typically, the dimensions inchesof the foam core board are either 20×30 inches or 30×40 inches.

The photographs, photocopies, and tear sheets should complement the designer's color story. To make the best impression, assemble the board using the proper artist supply materials. Remember, when boards are presented, the audience will be several feet away. Therefore, make sure that visual materials are large enough to be easily seen by everyone in the audience. Strong visuals also should be chosen to create an effective, immediate impression.

Make sure the following visual materials are included:

1. One or two photographs of the target customer
   - It is important to describe exactly who is going to be buying the final product.
2. Three to five images that depict the recommended theme or convey the mood trying to be created
   - Make sure these visuals are meaningful, that is, not vague.
3. Recommended trims or other objects
   - If a certain button style captures the gist of the design idea, attach a few buttons to the board. If a military feel is to be conveyed, attach a real epaulet and several medals.

Figure 3–1 shows a theme board that actually was used by the GIII Apparel Group to conceptualize a line. Note the tear sheet of a woman wearing a shearling coat. She represents the intended customer. The three remaining tear sheets convey a wild, rough, savage feeling, with the overall theme evoking a rugged, textured look.

FIGURE 3–1

An example of a theme board. (Courtesy of GIII Apparel Group)

The board in Figure 3–1 features several real-leather swatches, including buffalo split, distressed cow, oily cow, calfsplit, rugged leather, embossed crocodile leather, and deer.

Figure 3–1 also shows how artist's materials or objects may be used to illustrate a desired mood. The choice of paper can help define the theme. Note that a textured paper with ragged edges helps evoke the rough and rugged aspect of the concept.

The use of color, lettering, and graphics also is useful. Figure 3–1 incorporates neutral-colored papers to emphasize the earth tone color palette of the leathers and suedes used in the theme board.

TIPS FOR MAKING AN INTERESTING THEME BOARD. There are many ways one can approach designing a theme board. Specific ideas follow to make it interesting and effective:

- Carefully plan the layout of the theme board. Experiment with positioning the photographs, tear sheets, swatches, and other materials in different places on the board until the best result has been achieved. The theme board should be visually exciting as well as able to effectively convey the designer's message.
- Always include several swatches of recommended skins. Make sure the swatches are cut large enough so the intended audience will be able to distinguish individual characteristics. Swatches should not be smaller than 2×3 inches. A three-dimensional quality can be created on the board if swatches are artfully arranged and/or occasionally folded, as shown in Figure 3–1. If patterned or printed skins are used, swatches should be large enough to effectively show the complete pattern. Sometimes designers mount swatches on theme boards with Velcro®, which makes it easier for the audience to remove swatches for a detailed inspection.

Designing and Merchandising the Collection

Different designers initiate the design process in different ways. Some begin having been inspired by a particular skin or material.

In Figure 3–2, the designer first chose a skin called "Bubble Lamb" and let the choice of skin inspire a number of initial sketches.

Other designers begin by designing into a theme

The designer who created the final style board in Figure 3–3

FIGURE 3–2

Sketches inspired by a particular skin

used the theme board in Figure 3–1 for inspiration. Style boards will be discussed later in the book.

In either case, most designers start by doing rough sketches first. Once they feel comfortable with a particular direction, they focus on perfecting those sketches they feel will work.

Some designers mount all of their rough sketches on a wall, as shown in Figure 3–4, before beginning the editing process.

MERCHANDISING THE COLLECTION

A good designer will merchandise his or her individual designs into appropriate groups, being careful to create a balance within each group.

For instance, a balanced line of outerwear would include a range of styles within each group, such as short jackets, medium-length coats, three-quarter-length coats, and long coats. The line also will include a balanced assortment of collar treatments, such as notch, fur-trimmed, banded, hooded, and so on.

The style board in Figure 3–3 boasts two well-balanced outer-wear groups.

The merchandising objective behind the creation of well-balanced groups is to maximize sales by motivating a buyer to buy several styles within a group. For example, if a buyer is offered only a range of short jackets, he or she will then concentrate on deciding which one of the short jackets to buy. However, if a buyer is offered several groups, each consisting of one short jacket, one three-quarter-length coat, and one long coat, he or she will tend to concentrate on deciding which entire group of three styles to buy. In the end, by presenting a balanced collection, the designer is more likely to make three sales from each buyer instead of only one.

The same principles apply to merchandising sportswear, except that each group should be balanced by offering a variety of looks and combinations.

STYLE BOARD.   The style board includes flat sketches of all of the styles in a particular theme. Generally, the sketches show both the

FIGURE 3–3

Sketches inspired by a theme board (Courtesy of GIII Apparel Group)

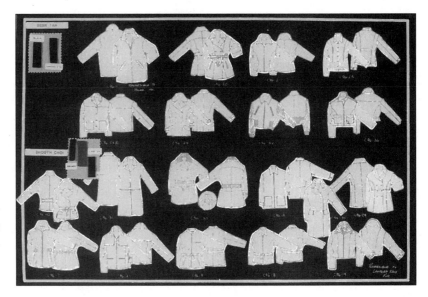

FIGURE 3–4

Several rough sketches from the early part of the design process. (Courtesy of GIII Apparel Group)

front and back views of each garment. They should be large enough to view the details of each garment, that is, never smaller than 3 × 4 inches each. However, sometimes style boards depict certain styles on a fashion figure for a more dramatic effect. The board must always include color swatches and style numbers. See Figure 3–3 for a good example of a style board.

For large collections, designers generally present both a theme and a style board to fully present their design concepts.

For smaller groups, many designers combine their theme and style boards. The Siena Studio Presentation Board in Figure 3–4 includes all of the key information that would normally be found in Siena's theme and style boards.

It depicts:

- the target customer
- the featured skin ("Bubble Lamb")
- the color story
- the mood
- the styles offered in the line

A collection that is well-researched, designed, and presented with theme and style boards can ensure a company both increased sales and reduced costs. The boards act as organizational tools for designers, selling platforms for salespeople, and merchandising aids for buyers. They also can stop a manufacturer from proceeding with a poorly conceived line before it is too late, that is, before precious production time is wasted and expensive samples are made.

The Remaining Steps in the Design Process

Once the best styles have been approved for sample making, the process is as follows:

1. The pattern maker makes the pattern.
2. The sample maker sews a muslin or canvas prototype.
3. The designer fits the muslin and makes any needed corrections.
4. The sample maker cuts and sews the garment using production skins.
5. The designer fits the final sample and makes and additional adjustment.

When a company manufactures overseas, the process is different. Once the designer creates the garment and it is approved for sample making, the process is as follows:

1. The designer completes a design/spec sheet that specifies everything the overseas pattern maker needs to know about the design, including exactly which skin or skins to use. (See Chapter 5, on Creating a Design/Spec Sheet, for examples.)
2. The overseas factory will follow the design/spec sheet and return the sewn sample in the specified skin.
3. The designer will find and inspect the garment and tell the overseas factory what corrections need to be made.
4. The overseas factory will continue to revise the garment until the designer is happy with it.

Planning

Planning the Design and Selecting the Skin

The designer should be aware of several points when designing in leather or suede. The most important consideration is the type of skin that will most enhance the design.

HAND

Just as a soft fabric would be chosen to create a drapey blouse, a soft lamb suede would be chosen to create a wonderfully soft, sexy suede shirt. Similarly, to create a tight-fitting skirt with a lot of stitching detail, a stiffer skin, such as pig suede, should be selected. The overall feel of a skin, that is, its stiffness versus its softness, is known at its **hand**.

WEIGHT

The weight of a skin is closely related to its hand. Skins vary in weight from animal to animal. The **weight** of a skin is defined as the number of ounces per square food of skin. Generally, a square foot of leather weighing one ounce tends to be about $\frac{1}{64}$ inch, or 0.4 mm.,

TABLE 4-1 LEATHER THICKNESS BY WEIGHT		
Inches	**Millimeters**	**Weight (Ounces)**
1/64	0.4	1
1/32	0.8	2
3/64	1.2	3
1/16	1.6	4
5/64	2.0	5
3/32	2.4	6
7/64	2.8	7

TABLE 4-2   "ODD" MEASUREMENTS
1 ounce = 0.4 millimeters
¼ ounce = 0.1 millimeters
2½ ounces = 1.0 millimeters

thick. If a two-ounce skin is ordered, the skin will be about $\frac{1}{32}$ of an inch (or 0.8 mm) thick, that is, twice as thick as a one-ounce skin. Most vendors want to talk in terms of millimeters instead of fractions of inches.

Table 4–1 provides a conversion estimate of weight to thickness.

Some simple rules follow in Table 4–2 for determining weights and thicknesses for odd measurements.

Skins that are heavier than 0.9 mm are rarely used in garment making. A typical leather shirt will be about 0.5–0.6 mm thick, an average leather part skin about 0.7–0.8 mm thick, and leather outerwear about 0.8–0.9 mm thick.

When purchasing the leather for a long, full skirt, low-weight lambskin should be chosen over pigskin. However, when making a pair of suede jeans, pig suede may be chosen over lamb suede for its weight and durability.

SKIN SIZE

Skin size varies from animal to animal. The term **skin** applies to the pelt of a small animal. The pelt on a large animal is called the

hide. Some skins, such as goat, can be as small as 2 square feet per entire skin. Yet, an entire cow skin can be as large as 60 square feet. In fact, because of the extremely large size of horse, cow, and buffalo skins, most tanneries cut them in half, down the back, before shipping them to manufacturers. Manufacturers and tanneries refer to these half hides as **side leather**.

The size of a skin often defines how many **cuts** or **cutlines** (the seams required to make a garment) will be needed in a design. Obviously, if a long goat suede coat is going to be created, there will be more seams (or cuts) than with larger skins. To specifically avoid cut lines in a garment, select a larger skin, such as pig, cow, or horse. Because leather and suede is costly, the price of the garment can be reduced by increasing the number of cuts used in it. Pattern pieces can be viewed as puzzle pieces. The smaller they are, the easier they are to interlock, thereby utilizing all of the skin. The larger the pattern pieces, the more difficult it will be to interlock them, which will result in a lot of leftover, wasted skin.

It is very important to make the cuts part of the design.

There is nothing less attractive than a garment that has ill-placed cuts. Poorly thought-out cuts can in fact ruin an otherwise beautiful garment, which will be discussed later in this book.

SKIN MEASURING

The standard system of measurement is by the square foot. Since skins are not square but have an irregular shape, it is impossible for tanneries to measure a perfectly square foot. Therefore, measuring machines are used (Figure 4–1). Two numbers are stamped on the backs of the skins. Usually, the first number is much larger than the second number so they can be read more easily. The first number is the full square footage. The small, second number is the remaining percentage of a square foot, represented in quarters. For example "51" would be 5¼ or 5¼ square feet. "52" is 5½ square feet and "53" is 5¾ square feet.

When calculating the consumption of the design, estimate the average size of the skins that will be used, then use the pattern pieces to estimate how many skins will be needed to create each garment. For example, if the average size of an English domestic leather skin is seven square feet, draw an area on paper equivalent to 7 square feet. This would normally be a rectangle approximately 2 × 3½ feet. Lay the

FIGURE 4–1

Measuring machine

pattern parts on top of the "skin." Once the skin is covered with as many pattern pieces as possible, set those pieces aside and lay the remaining pattern pieces on the skin. When all of the pattern pieces have been used, add up the total skin footage used.

Remember, leather/suede skins are natural products. There may be scars, hole, wrinkles, and other undesirable small or large blemishes on the skins.

To allow for the inevitable blemishes and holes in the skins, add extra footage to the calculations. Add an allowance of 10 percent if low-quality skins will be used. Add an allowance of 5 percent if high-quality skins will be used.

To translate an existing fabric design into leather, calculate the leather footage required by using the following formulas in Table 4–3.

TABLE 4–3		
Fabric Garment		**Leather Garment Roughly Equivalent Leather Footage**
Fabric Width Used	**Fabric Length Used**	
54 Inches	1 Yard	13 Square Feet
36 Inches	1 Yard	9 Square Feet
* Always add the 5 to 10 percent waste allowance to any fabric-to-leather translation.		

SKIN CHARACTERISTICS. The following chart describes the key characteristics of different types of leather or suede.

SUEDE TYPE	SKIN SIZE (sq. ft.)	WEIGHT (oz.)	CHARACTERISTICS
CHARACTERISTICS OF DIFFERENT TYPES OF LEATHER			
Antelope	5 – 9	2 – 3	Very fine, lightweight, velvety nap; soft
Buckskin	7 – 9	2 – 4	Originally made of buckskin or deerskin. Now made of calfskin or sheepskin; soft, strong, and durable
Chamois	7 – 9	2 – 3	Originally made from antelope skin; now made from the underside of sheep, lamb, or calf. Tanned with fish oil or cod liver oil to make it stronger and more resilient; soft, light, small skins; pale-yellow in color; washable
Lamb suede	5 – 7	2 – 3	Made from young sheep or lamb. Soft, very fine, fluid, and drapey
Sheepskin	7 – 9	2 – 3	Similar texture and appearance to lambskin
Split	18 – 25	2 – 3½	Made when a thick cowskin is split into two thinner skins; characterized by being sueded on both sides; rough texture, strong
Pig suede	9 – 16	3 – 4	The skin is characterized by groups of three tiny holes, caused by removal of the animal's hair; strong, durable and firm; less expensive than lamb suede, but more expensive than cow split
Pig split	9 – 16	3 – 4	Made when a thick pigskin is split into two thinner skins; characterized by being sueded on both sides; rough texture, strong, durable, and firm
Kidskin	3 – 6	1 – 2	Made from a young goat; soft and pliable; not always sueded
Goat suede	4 – 6	2 – 3	From a mature goat; soft, but not as soft as lamb suede; skins are smaller than lamb and are more dense

CHARACTERISTICS OF DIFFERENT TYPES OF LEATHER (continued)

LEATHER TYPE	SKIN SIZE (sq. ft.)	WEIGHT (oz.)	CHARACTERISTICS
Calfskin	9 – 15	1½ – 4	Made from the skin of young cows; close, fine smooth grain
Capeskin	3 – 9	1½ – 3	Made from South African hair or wool sheep; soft, but strong
Cabretta	5 – 9	2 – 3	Spanish work meaning "goat"; now made from a South American hair sheep rather than a wool-type sheep; smooth, pliant, but tends to stretch
Cowhide	18 – 25	12 – 3½	Strong firm, durable, and thick; not as smooth as calfskin; less expensive than lamb or calf
Doeskin	3 – 5	1 – 2	Usually lambskin or sheepskin. Light, soft, supple, fine suede finish; washable
Deerskin	9	3 – 4	Made from elk and deer with the grain left intact; tanned in fish oil; soft, but strong; has a yellow-beige tint; washable
Horse	25 – 35	1½ – 4	A rough-type skin, with lots of blemishes and irregular shading (unless pigmented); "shell cordovan" comes from a horse's hind quarters; pony skins are 25 sq. ft., horse skins are 35 (+) sq. ft.
Pigskin	9 – 16	3 – 4	Distinctive surface grain; tough, durable
Ostrich	12 – 14	2 – 3	Bird skin known for the small bumps left on the skin once the feathers are removed; this effect is often seen on embossed leathers; comes from South Africa, Israel, and Zimbabwe
Peccary	9 – 16	3 – 4	Central and South American wild boar; looks like pigskin
Hair sheep	4 – 6	½ – 1	Sheep whose wool is hair-like
Lambskin	5 – 7	½ – 1	Skin from a lamb or young sheep
Kidskin	9 – 15	1½ – 4	Male or female bovine skin, sized between a calf and a mature animal
Shearling	5 – 7	1 – 2	Wooled lambskins and sheep with the wool intact

CHARACTERISTICS OF DIFFERENT TYPES OF LEATHER (continued)

LEATHER (continued)

TYPE	SKIN SIZE (sq. ft.)	WEIGHT (oz.)	CHARACTERISTICS
Goat leather	4 – 6	2 – 3	The grainy side has a raspy feel
Veal	9 – 15	1½ – 4	A large calfskin
English domestic	5–7	½ – 1	Lambskin from England; a tight, clean- looking skin
New Zealand lamb	5–7	½ – 1	Lambskin from New Zealand; grainy and easier to stretch than English domestic
Cobra	3 – 4	½	Large snake from Asia and Southeast Asia
Lizard	1 – 1½	1	Has tiny scales; usually comes from South America and Indonesia
Sharkskin	1½ – 7	1½ – 3	Has small scales, usually brown or white or black and white; very durable; comes from the Caribbean and Gulf of Mexico
Elephant	8 – 10/pc.	2 – 8	Very thick, tough skins, usually gray or brown; uneven skin
Hippopotamus	various	2 – 8	Large, unique grain; **Note:** sold in sections of various sizes
Anaconda	6 – 9	1½	South American; Note: May be endangered

NOVELTY SKINS

TYPE	CHARACTERISTIC
Patent leather	Any leather treated with a waterproof film on one surface; the treated surface is lustrous and reflective
Pearlized leather	Any leather that has been given a colored, pearl-like luster
Embossed leather	Any leather that has a motif in relief; the embossing is achieved with a metal template, heat, and pressure
Printed leather suede	Skins that have been silk screened or painted
Distressed leather	Skins that have been treated to look worn and rough; manufacturers achieve this either by a mechanical process or by screen printing
Nu-buck	A skin whose grain side has been buffed; often used on lamb, cow, or calf; the resulting skin looks like suede, but with a tight, low pile

CHARACTERISTICS OF DIFFERENT TYPES OF LEATHER (continued)

SPECIALTY SKINS

NOTE: Specialty skins are not usually sold by weight. When you buy these skins, you can expect relatively consistent weights from skin to skin.

TYPE	SKIN SIZE (sq. ft.)	WEIGHT (oz.)	CHARACTERISTICS
Alligator	6 – 14	N/A	These skins are banned for conservation reasons
Python	8 – 20	N/A	A large snakeskin (up to 30" long) used mostly for bags, shoes, and boots
Sealskin	See Note	N/A	Black, shiny leather; **Note:** Endangered. Do not use!
Fish	1 – 2	N/A	Usually salmon, carp, or cod
Whip snake	6	N/A	Indian water snakes; fairly inexpensive; excellent for trims

PURCHASING SKIN.   Skins should almost always be purchased in person, which require traveling to faraway places, at great expense. But, if quantities of skins are being purchased, money could actually be saved. When inspecting skins, be aware of the following:

- Be certain the skin being shown is the one requested. Sometimes, a dealer will try to pass off one skin as another. A less-than-knowledgeable buyer may be tricked. The characteristics chart in this book should be studied to ensure familiarity with a particular skin.
- Smell the skin. Does it have an obnoxious odor? Some improperly tanned skins have a bad odor that cannot be eliminated by dry cleaning.

Refer to Figure 4–2, which names the various sections of a leather skin.

- When examining a skin, remember that the nappa, or outside, of the skin should be the best quality part of the skin. If it has excessive scars, holes, or miscolorations, it is not a high-caliber skin.

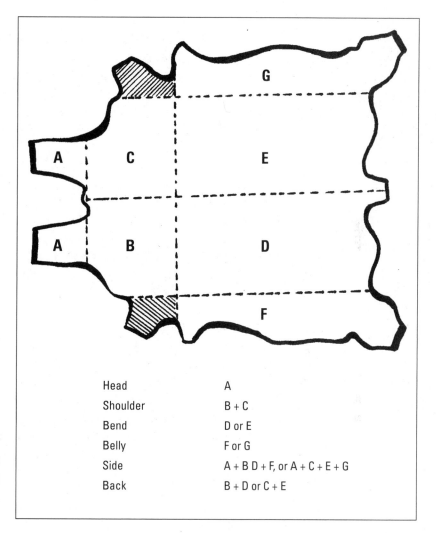

Head	A
Shoulder	B + C
Bend	D or E
Belly	F or G
Side	A + B D + F, or A + C + E + G
Back	B + D or C + E

FIGURE 4–2

Names of the different parts of a leather skin

Expect to find weak spots, stretched areas, stains, or shading in the belly, neck, and leg areas of the skin. Yet, despite these imperfections, clever cutters often make good use of these sections by including them in the hidden parts of a garment or in highly decorated accessories.

- Watch out for tiny holes in the skin. They may not be visible if the skin is examined on a table. In order to detect this problem, hold the skin up to the light. Small holes become larger over time and can ruin finished garments.

- Uneven dyeing causes **shading**. Shading exists when different parts of a skin show variations in color. Shading makes it impossible to match different sections of a garment when sewing it together. Accept minor shading differences in full aniline skins. Semi-aniline skins also will have shading problems, although probably less than aniline skins due to their special spray processing.

- Choose skins with roughly the same weight. Skins often vary within the same bundle.

- Make sure the grain or surface of the skins has continuity. Some skins are more grainy than others. Fine garments should boast a uniform grain.

- Match the colors on all of the skins. Because there may be different shades of the same color in one bundle, always lay the skins out by folding them in half and placing them on top of each other with about 6″ of each skin showing. This way the skins can be viewed at a glance.

- Calculate how many skins will be needed for a design and purchase more than that number of skins. Skins that have many blemished will produce a poor yield. Always buy more skins than needed, since it may not be possible to obtain replacement skins in the proper shade at a later date.

- Make sure, when ordering skins by mail or phone, that you clearly communicate the type and quality of skins you require. If the supplier doesn't have the skins you need and offers you a substitute, ask the supplier to send you a sample of the skin for your approval before placing your order. Always specify which skin size you want. If you plan on cutting 6 sq. ft. skins and they send you 4 sq. ft. skins, you might not have enough raw skins to complete your production run.

- Generally, skins are purchased according to a percentage breakdown of "A", "B", or "C" quality skins. Some suppliers refer to them as "1st", "2nd", or "3rd" quality skins. They might even be described as "Type #1, Type #2," and so on. A typical selection might be either 60 percent As, 30 percent Bs, and 10 percent Cs or 50 percent As, 30 percent Bs, and 20 percent Cs, however, the percentage breakdown will vary from tannery to tannery.

- Tanneries often combine the three grades of skins within a bundle; this is known as a "table run."

- A **bundle** is defined as a twelve-skin unit. It usually comes rolled and tied. A **pack** usually represents approximately 3,000 square feet of leather. Tanneries ship packs in large boxes containing bundles. When buying a small quantity, such as 40 square feet, a dealer may not want to break open a whole bundle and may request that the entire bundle be purchased.

• When buying only "A" or 1st quality skins, most suppliers charge a price premium of +30 percent, unless they are dealing with a long-term customer or are purchasing huge quantities. Some dealers may not even sell small quantities of exclusive "A" quality skins.

PLANNING THE DESIGN. When working with your own or a commercial pattern from one of the major pattern companies, for example, *Simplicity, Vogue,* or *McCalls,* the following points should be noted:

1. *Think* before you start making your patterns and especially before you purchase your skins. Think about the end user, the person who will eventually buy your garment.
2. If you plan to use extremely thin skins, remember that your purchaser will find it quite easy to scuff or scrape such skins, increasing the probability of returns. A heavier skin, although not as fashionable, will wear much better over time.
3. Will your purchaser be able to clean your garment without risk?

   • Avoid combining highly contrasting colors, for example, black with white, unless you have personally confirmed that the darker color's dyes will not run into the lighter colored sections when the garment is dry cleaned. Use the **white handkerchief test** to confirm the stability of a garment's color. Rub the handkerchief along the inner facing of the garment. The color should not easily come off.
   • Do not attach hardware to your garment, for example, heavy metal ornaments, which will not be able to survive repeated cleaning.

4. Have you properly matched your choice of animal skin to the type of garment you plan to design? For example, if you are designing a coat, do not select lamb suede as its skin because it is too delicate and would not wear as well as perhaps lamb leather. You might use a 0.4–0.5 mm thick pig suede for a shirt, but not for a fitted skirt, or a 0.7–0.8 mm thick pig suede for a skirt, but not for a shirt.

5. Always make a muslin of your garment, whether you plan to use the flat pattern method, the draping method, or a commercial pattern. By making a muslin first, you can always make needed adjustments to the muslin before you cut the skins. (See Figures 4–3 and 4–4.)

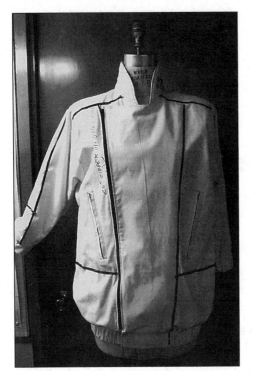

FIGURE 4–3

Front of a muslin using styling tape to denote cuts

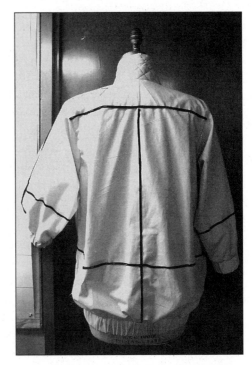

FIGURE 4–4

Back of a muslin showing styling tape to denote cuts

Once a pattern is cut, adjustments cannot easily be made. You particularly do not want to repair a garment after it has been sewn. Inevitably, the resown garment will show some of its old sewing holes.

Suede is a little more forgiving. The holes created when sewing a suede garment are relatively small. Creating a muslin that fits before cutting will prevent repairs to the brand-new garment. This **fitting muslin** will enable you to confirm the appropriateness of the placement of the cuts in the garment, if they are required, for that type of leather.

Using styling tape, place the cut lines. Make sure they are placed where they will be the least noticeable, unless they are being used as design details. (Again, see Figures 4–3 and 4–4.)

Make enough cuts to best utilize the size of your skins. Always ask yourself if any of your pattern pieces will be bigger than the average high-quality portion of the skins.

Try to avoid placing cut lines at stress points in the garment. Do not place a cut line on the knee area of a trouser. Always place it above or below the knee. There are also some aesthetic considerations. For example, cut lines at the hip and thigh level on a skirt or pant tend to make women look wider in that area.

The more cut lines that are added to the garment, the less skin will be used because you will be able to fit more tightly interlocked pieces from each single skin, just like a jigsaw puzzle. Figure 4–5 illustrates an example of poor skin utilization.

Figure 4–6, however, shows that by adding a cut line to the same design, dividing the front and back leg of the shorts, more pattern pieces can be obtained from the same skin. Once a decision has been made about where to place the cut lines, a hard pattern is then created.

In a typical leather garment factory, where several hundred garments might be cut from one pattern, a hard cardboard template is made from the original pattern. The factory uses an electric cardboard pattern cutter, a special electric saw, such as the Stanley Industrial Unishear, to create these durable pattern pieces. (See Figure 4–7.)

Even if you wish to cut smaller quantities of skin, you should make (and use) an **oak tag pattern**. (See Figure 4–8.) Hard patterns provide better cutting stability, allowing sharp, clean edges to be cut. A hard copy of a commercial pattern should always be made. The paper on which commercial patterns are printed is essentially tissue paper. Without copying it to hard pattern, it will deteriorate quickly.

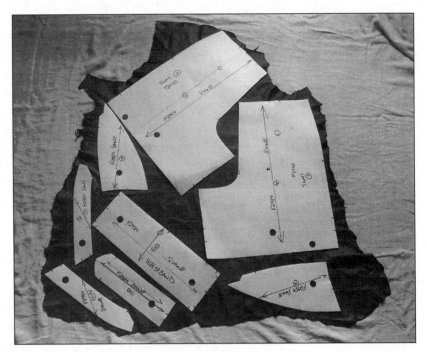

FIGURE 4–5

Poor utilization of skin

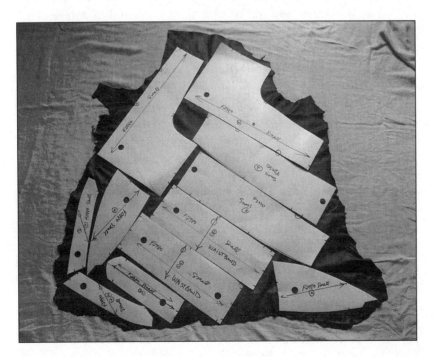

FIGURE 4–6

Better utilization of skin

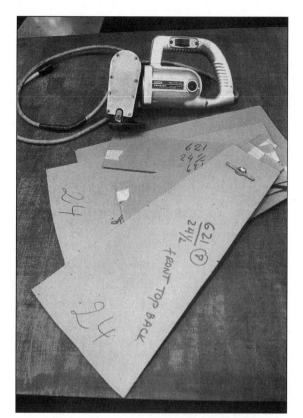

FIGURE 4–7

Electric cardboard pattern cutter and cardboard pattern

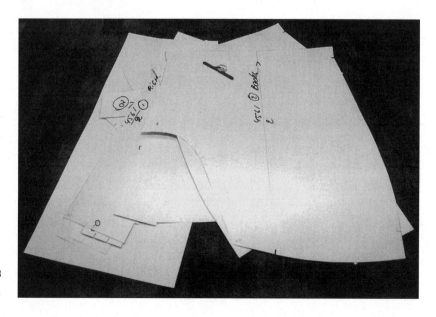

FIGURE 4–8

Oak tag pattern

To make a hard pattern, obtain a piece of oak tag or any other thick, firm paper. Fold the paper into a double layer. Staple the free edges together then cut the doubled-over paper into the proper pattern shape.

Seam allowances should be about ½″ for most seams. However, a ¼″ seam allowance should be provided for seams that are stitched and turned, for example, collar edges and pocket flaps.

Creating a Design/ Spec Sheet

Many manufacturers are importing leather garments from around the world from countries such as Mexico, India, China, and Korea.

Some companies will make a prototype sample of a garment, then send that sample to the manufacturer, which might be located in another country. Other companies send their manufacturers a design/spec sheet only. The factory will make the first prototype by reading the design/spec sheet and following its instructions. There are many specifications listed on the sheets. The more measurements that are provided to the person making the pattern in a manufacturing facility, the more accurate the first sample will be.

The process involves the following steps:

1. The designer either faxes, mails, or hand delivers the design/ spec sheet to the pattern maker at the factory.
2. The pattern maker makes a pattern and a first sample or prototype from the design/spec sheet.
3. The designer then examines the first sample for construction, size specifications, and the overall "look."
4. The designer notes any corrections directly on the design/spec sheet under the category "Second Prototype" and returns it to the pattern maker at the factory.

5. The pattern maker makes further corrections in the original prototype, or creates a new one, then sends the second prototype back to the designer.
6. If necessary, the process may continue to a third or fourth prototype. But usually the style is fully corrected by the second.
7. The factory makes a final production sample for reference.

In the pages that follow, a design/spec sheet is found for a basic shirt. This form also can be used to define the specs of a jacket and/or a coat.

Design/Spec Sheet: Shirt/Jacket/Coat

Company: Skin:	Design Instinct Lamb suede	Style #: Date:	5039 12/6/95
Garment Description:	Women's Basic Shirt	Label:	Design Instinct
County of Origin:	Korea	Hangtag:	Design Instinct

Shell		Contrast A		Contrast B		Contrast C	
Color:	Red	Color:		Color		Color:	

Lining		Interlining		Interfacing		Pocketing	
Body (Upper): Rayon/acetate		Body:					
Body (Lower)							
Sleeves	None	Sleeves		Tricot			
Trim							
Button:		#2199 L/24 - 7 total		Knit:			
Snap:				Velcro:			
Zipper:				Fur trim:			
Pull:				Elastic:			
Drawstring:				Buckle:			
Eyelet:				Shoulder pad:			
Stopper:				Contrast topstitch:			

Sketch:

Design/Spec Sheet: Shirt/Jacket/Coat (continued)

Size Specifications Size: *Medium*	Prototype	2nd Prototype	Production Sample
Dates:	12/5/95		
Body length @ center back:	29		
Center back waist length:			
Across back shoulder	21		
Across back shoulder 5″ down CB	19		
Shoulder slope	$7^3/_4$		
Waist extended ½	23½		
Waist relaxed ½			
Bottom width ½	23		
Depth of armhole			
Armhole front curve	10		
Armhole back curve	10¼		
Sleeve length from shoulder	29½		
Sleeve length from CB	32½		
Sleeve muscle 1″ down armhole ½	$8^3/_4$		
Sleeve 2″ above edge/cuff ½	6¼		
Sleeve opening ½	6		
Cuff height			
Across front raglan			
10″ down from HPS			
Across back raglan			
10″ down from HPS			
Armhole front raglan			
Armhole back raglan			
Bust/chest ½ 1″ down armhole	23		
Neck opening inside	5		
Neckline from notch to notch			

Design/Spec Sheet: Shirt/Jacket/Coat (continued)

Size Specifications Size: *Medium*	Prototype	2nd Prototype	Production Sample
Dates:	12/5/95		
Front neck drop (HPS)	2½		
Back neck drop (HPS)	½		
Collar height at CB	2½		
Collar stand	1¼		
Collar height at CF			
Collar point	3⅛		
Lapel point			
Placket width			
Placket length			
Yoke height front (HPS)			
Yoke height back (HPS)			
Chest pocket from HPS			
Chest pocket from CF	9¼		
Body pocket from HPS	3½		
Body pocket from CF			
Upper pocket flap width/length			
Upper pocket width/length			
Lower pocket width/length			
Lower pocket flap width/length			
Pocket welt width/length			

Comments/Special Sewing Instructions: *Self-color edgestitch around collar and center front, shirt tail bottom, collar stand, and pocket. Topstitch sleeve hem 1″ from edge.*

In the pages that follow, a design/spec sheet is found for a drawstring jacket. The same form used for the above shirt is used for the jacket.

Design/Spec Sheet: Shirt/Jacket/Coat

Company: Skin:	Design Instinct Lamb leather		Style #: Date:	3066 3/9/93
Garment Description:	Men's Drawstring Jacket		Label:	Design Instinct
County of Origin:	India		Hangtag:	Design Instinct

Shell		Contrast A		Contrast B		Contrast C	
Color:	Black	Color:		Color		Color:	

Lining		Interlining		Interfacing		Pocketing	
Body (Upper): Flannel		Body: Thinsulate		Tricot		Twill acetate	
Body (Lower) Twill acetate							
Sleeves	Twill acetate	Sleeves	Thin- sulate				
Trim	#2 tape						

Button:		Knit:	
Snap:	#6119 1/3-9 total	Velcro:	
Zipper:	25" DTM plastic #5	Fur trim:	
Pull:	#209 DTM	Elastic:	
Drawstring:	#29 DTM	Buckle:	
Eyelet:		Shoulder pad:	
Stopper:		Contrast topstitch:	

Sketch:

Design/Spec Sheet: Shirt/Jacket/Coat (continued)

Size Specifications Size: *Medium*	Prototype	2nd Prototype	Production Sample
Dates:	10/10/93		
Body length @ center back:	34		
Center back waist length:	20		
Across back shoulder			
Across back shoulder 5″ down CB			
Shoulder slope			
Waist extended ½	25½		
Waist relaxed ½			
Bottom width ½	25½		
Depth of armhole			
Armhole front curve			
Armhole back curve			
Sleeve length from shoulder	32¼		
Sleeve length from CB	37		
Sleeve muscle 1″ down armhole ½	12		
Sleeve 2″ above edge/cuff ½	7¼		
Sleeve opening ½	4¼		
Cuff height	2¼		
Across front raglan 10″ down from HPS	22		
Across back raglan 10″ down from HPS	22½		
Armhole front raglan	16½		
Armhole back raglan	19¾		
Bust/chest ½ 1″ down armhole	27		
Neck opening inside	6		
Neckline from notch to notch			

Design/Spec Sheet: Shirt/Jacket/Coat (continued)			
Size Specifications Size: *Medium*	Prototype	2nd Prototype	Production Sample
Dates:	10/10/93		
Front neck drop (HPS)	5¼		
Back neck drop (HPS)	½		
Collar height at CB	4		
Collar stand			
Collar height at CG			
Collar point	3¾		
Lapel point			
Placket width	2¾		
Placket length	28¾		
Yoke height front (HPS)			
Yoke height back (HPS)			
Chest pocket from HPS	11½		
Chest pocket from CF	7½		
Body pocket from HPS	22¾		
Body pocket from CF	2¾		
Upper pocket flap width/length	2½ × 7		
Upper pocket width/length			
Lower pocket width/length			
Lower pocket flap width/length	8 × 3		
Pocket welt width/length	¾ × 6		

Comments/Special Sewing Instructions: *Self-color double needle topstitch: collar, placket, pocket flaps, cuffs, shoulder seam, center back seam. Decorative zigzag stitch on front placket and collar, width of placket 4⅛" wide apart. Edgestitch waist seam and around welt pocket. Open seams on sleeves. Topstitch ¾" up from hem on sleeves.*

In the pages that follow, a design/spec sheet is found for a pair of pants or a skirt. This form also might be used for a pair of pleated pants.

Design/Spec Sheet: Pants/Skirt

Company: Skin:	Design Instinct Lamb leather		Style #: Date:	3221 10/18/95
Garment Description:	Women's Pleated Pant		Label:	Design Instinct
County of Origin:	China		Hangtag:	Design Instinct

Shell		Contrast A		Contrast B		Contrast C	
Color:	Brown	Color:		Color		Color:	

Lining Body	Body Interlining	Pocketing	Interfacing
Rayon/acetate			Tricot

Button:	#5641 DTM-1 total	Knit:	
Snap:		Velcro:	
Zipper:	1 – 8" DTM	Elastic:	
Pull:		Buckle:	
Drawstring:		Contrast topstitch:	
Eyelet:		Stopper:	

Sketch:

Design/Spec Sheet: Pants/Skirt (continued)

Size Specifications Size: *Medium*	Prototype	2nd Prototype	Production Sample
Dates:	11/7/95		
Waist	28		
Front rise below waistband	12		
Back rise below waistband	14		
Thigh 1″ below crotch seam ½	13		
Knee 12″ below crotch seam ½	10		
Leg opening ½	7		
Inseam length	31		
Outseam length	42½		
Belt loop width/length	³⁄₈ × 1³⁄₄		
Waistband length edge to edge ½	15		
High hip 4″ below waistband ½	18½		
Hip at 7″ below WBN ½	2½		
Skirt length below WBN			
Sweep ½			
Pocket width	½		
Pocket length	5⁵⁄₈		

Comments/Special Sewing Instructions: *Self-color edgestitch: around pocket welt, waistband loop edges, and fly front. Bound buttonhole on waistband. Pant is fully lined.*

Chapter

6

Sorting, Shading, and Cutting

Sorting and Shading

Before a garment is cut, the skins that will be used must be sorted to ensure that all of the pieces look the same, that is, have the same color and graininess. If a design requires 40 square feet of leather, 48 to 50 square feet of skins should be selected and then checked for grain and color consistency.

As discussed earlier, each skin should be folded in half along the lengthwise grain and overlapped on top of each other, allowing about six inches of each skin to show. (See Figure 6–1.) This will allow the skins to be seen at a glance, simulating how they might look in one garment. Proper lighting should be used when evaluating skin colors; ideally, good overhead concentrated light is best.

Cutting

The manufacturers of leather and suede garments cut one skin at a time. Manufacturers of fabric garments usually ply several layers of fabric on top of each other before cutting. But because leather skins vary so dramatically in size and quality, manufacturers always

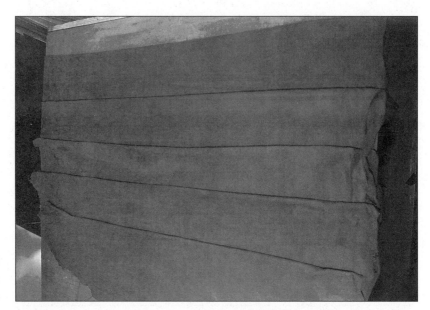

FIGURE 6–1

How to confirm color consistency

FIGURE 6–2

Leather cutting board

cut skins individually, placing a pattern piece on top of each skin. (Never try to cut two pieces at once by folding a skin in half.)

Leather garment manufacturers cut leathers on a special wooden leather cutting board. (See Figure 6–2.) They use a **short knife**, sharpened on a special sharpening stone, to actually cut the skins. (See Figure 6–3.) Leather cutters like to use a short knife because it is small and fits nicely into the palm of the hand. It also has replaceable blades, making it easier to quickly replace dull blades.

A professional leather cutter places each pattern piece on the right side of a skin, the nappa or outside, avoiding any flaws. He or she holds the pattern down with one hand while cutting the skin, using the short knife, with his or her other hand. (See Figure 6–4.) A weight may also be used to hold down the pattern. An awl would

FIGURE 6–3

Short knife and sharpening stone

FIGURE 6–4

Cutting with short knife

then be used to poke small holes for darts and the short knife used to make the small cuts for notches.

The **marking and scissor method** is an alternative to the short knife method. Working with the same hard paper pattern, place the pattern on the right side of the skin. Place a weight on the pattern to keep it stable. (See Figure 6–5.)

Trace around the pattern piece with a pencil or fine-tipped, waterproof marking pen, marking all the notches. (See Figure 6–6.) Do not use an ink pen, as it will have a tendency to smudge. An awl may be used to mark the darts by puncturing small holes, but do not mark the darts with a pen since, when sewing, it is easier to see the markings on the "wrong side."

Once all of the parts have been marked, cut the pattern pieces using sharp dressmaker shears, either 7″ or 10″ length. Cut on the inside of the marking line because if this isn't done extra width and length may be added. Make certain that all of the notches are no more than ¼″ deep. If they are cut deeper than this, they may eventually cause the leather or suede to tear or split in that area.

Once all of the pieces have been cut, matching right sides together in pairs, roll them up and tie them together. This will keep the skins from creasing until they are ready to be sewn.

FIGURE 6–5

Using a weight to hold a pattern down while cutting

FIGURE 6–6

Marking with a pencil

Storing Skins

Never fold unused leather or suede. If it is folded, the creases along the fold lines may not come out. If possible, store them flat or draped over a padded surface. If not, they can be loosely rolled. (See Figure 6–7.) Place the right side (the nappa side) of two skins face to face, then roll them up together. Do not store them near heat or in the sun as they might dry out and fade. Overly dried-out skins become brittle and may easily tear.

Cutting Tips

Since the yield of each piece of leather is often too small to allow cutting both the left and right sides of, for instance, the front of a blouse from the same skin, you will often find yourself cutting several different and often unrelated pattern pieces from the same skin. When this is done make sure you do not forget what sides of the garment have already been cut. To help remember where you are in a cutting job, immediately flip over each left and right pattern piece just after it is cut, then set it aside. Make sure the already used pattern piece is set with the still-to-be-cut side facing up. When you've cut as much as you can from one skin, use the pattern pieces that were set aside to cut from the next skin. This process will enable you to remember which sides have already been cut and which sides have not.

As each pattern part is cut, keep in mind which part sits next to which in the garment. This will allow grains and colors to be easily matched. Also note that the stretchy areas of the skin should not be placed at the stress points of the garment or where they will be visible. The main sections of the garment should be cut with their vertical dimensions cut from the lengthwise dimension of the skin. This ensures that the left-to-right dimension of the garment utilizes the more stretchy, crosswise grain of the animal.

The smaller pieces can be laid either crosswise or lengthwise on the skin to gain the best skin yield. When cutting a printed or embossed skin, cut it so the design on each piece goes in the same direction. Some suedes, such as pig, boast a very definite nap "design." When working with such a suede, cut all of the pattern parts in the same direction.

Never stretch a skin to produce a bigger yield. If this is done, the parts will shrink back to their original shapes. As a result, the pattern parts will not easily fit together. The result will be an ill-fitting, poorly shaped garment.

FIGURE 6–7

*Cut pattern pieces
rolled up for storage*

Putting the Leather Garment Together

Stitching

A sewing machine that can handle the thickness and weight of skins must be used. Most home sewing machines will not be able to successfully handle the weight of most leathers. Professional sewing machines use a three-cord thread that is stronger than the regular cotton thread used to sew fabrics.

Use a walking foot machine, such as the Juki LU562 or the Juki LU563, for topstitching and sewing over several thicknesses of leather or suede. (See Figures 7–1 and 7–2.)

Another option is the Singer 31-19 or Singer 431 vibrating foot machine. These machines are good for sewing medium-thickness leathers or for closing seams. (See Figure 7–3.) They are especially made to handle the weight and thickness of leather skins. Otherwise, an industrial straight stitch machine should be used, such as the Juki DDL5530 or Singer 491.

If an industrial straight stitching machine is used, attach Teflon® teeth, foot, and plate to the machine. (See Figure 7–4.) The stitch size should be no larger than eight to ten stitches per inch. Smaller stitches will result in tearing at the stitching line. The proper needle for the machine is a tripoint or diamond point, size 16 or 18.

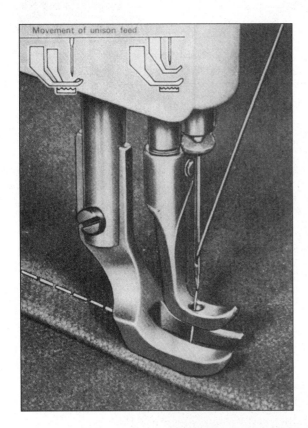

FIGURE 7–1

Needlebar: Walking Foot
Machine, Juki LU562.
(Courtesy of Juki America, Inc.)

FIGURE 7–2
Walking Foot Machine,
Juki LU563. (Courtesy of
Juki America, Inc.)

FIGURE 7–3
Singer 431
Vibrating Foot
Machine.
(Courtesy of
Singer)

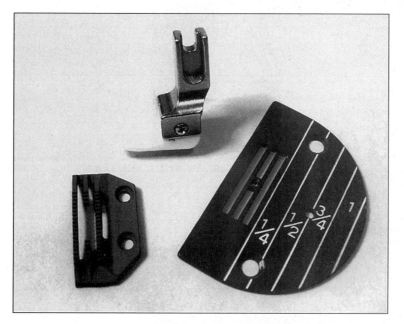

FIGURE 7–4
Teflon teeth, foot, and plate

When sewing by hand, use a glover's needle, which ranges in size from 2 to 8. Size 2 is perfect for hand sewing buttons and trims.

Gluing

Gluing makes seams lie flat and eliminates excess bulk. Glue is also used to drape and fold the skin for certain effects, which can create a beautiful, high-styled garment.

To apply glue to a seam, use a brush and a roller tool. (See Figure 7–5.) The glue used in leather factories is a white cement available at professional supply companies under a number of brand names, for example, Sobo®, Barge® cement, and Magnatac 809®. (See Appendix A.) Some factories use an oil can container to apply the glue. (See Figure 7–6.)

However, the effect of dry cleaning on these glues must be considered. Most leather cleaners can replace glue in accessible areas of the garment, for example, hems and seams. But they may not be able to replace the glue in draped areas. If possible, try to ensure that you design around this problem by machine or hand stitching these hidden areas.

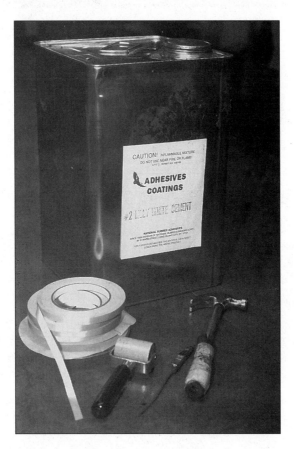

FIGURE 7–5

Glue, roller, brush,

hammer, and cold tape

FIGURE 7–6

Oil can used to apply glue

Pressing

Leather or suede should never be in direct contact with an iron. Always place heavy brown paper, such as a heavy brown grocery bag, between the iron and the garment to be pressed.

Avoid steam and do not use a pressing or muslin cloth. Use a medium-to-low setting on the iron and press the garment evenly. Do not let the iron sit in one spot, since this can create a permanent mark on the skin.

Lining, Underlining, and Interfacing

Lining

Making a lining pattern for a leather garment is like making a lining for a cloth garment. Leather garments are more often lined than cloth garments, since most people do not like the feel of animal skin against their skin. However, many designers will add only a half lining to a shirt by lining the upper portion of the shirt only.

Some skins, such as lamb suede, feel rough or look unsightly on the inside. Designers usually will add a lining to conceal the imperfections.

To make an unlined leather garment, purchase specially processed leathers with insides as nice as outsides.

Once a fitting muslin is made, decide whether you want to back certain parts of the garment with lining. For example, you may want to consider using a lining fabric for the undersides of the pocket flaps, epaulets, cuffs, collars, or hood. You also may want to use lining fabric only, that is, no leather at all, to line certain hidden sections of the garment, such as the underlay of a wrap skirt or the underneath top yoke area of a trenchcoat. This will not only save skins (and money), but it also will make the garment lighter.

Underlining

Based on the weight of the skins, you may wish to add extra firmness to certain areas of the garment. For example, use a fusible tricot interfacing to give a lamb suede blazer a more tailored look. Designers prefer tricot as an underlining (versus nonwoven and woven-fusible) because it is knitted, allowing it to stretch when the garment is worn.

Interlinings and Fillers

Interlinings are materials that are applied underneath the lining of garments, usually for additional warmth. Many manufacturers do this by either fully or partially insulating garments. These materials are known as fillers, and the two most popular product lines are made by 3M and DuPont.

Fillers are chosen based on their hand, feel, and the desired look of the garment. Some fillers are designed to provide a very thin layer of material, solely to provide warmth. Other fillers are designed to provide garments with a lofty, down-like look.

DuPont's insulation products range in weight from 100 to 200 grams and are made of Dacron® polyester fibers. The following is a list of the company's brand names:

Thin Insulation	Mid-loft Insulation	High-loft Insulation
Thermolite®	Thermoloft®	Microloftallofil®
Microloft®		Quallofil®
		Hallofil®
		Hallofil II®

3M's products are blends of polyolefin and polyester and range in weight from 40 to 250 grams. These include:

Thin Insulation	Mid-loft Insulation	High-loft Insulation
Thinsulate®	Thinsulate Ultra®	Thinsulate Lite Loft®
Thinsulate Lite Loft®		

Interfacing and Seam Reinforcement

Designers apply interfacing to all seams that are sewn together and turned, such as pocket flaps, welt pockets, pocket tops, collars, lapels, waistbands, cuffs, and the center fronts of garments.

Interfacings also are used to secure areas of stress in a garment, such as around the armholes, necklines, zippers, pocket openings, buttonholes, buttons, hems (sleeve and garment bottoms), and loops.

Several types of interfacing can be used, but the most preferred is fusible. You can purchase **fusible interfacing** in three types, nonwoven fusible (see Figure 8–1), woven fusible, and fusible tricot. To choose the correct interfacing, consider the type of skin being used and the design of the garment. For example, when designing a soft, lightweight lamb suede collar, a soft interfacing should be used. Therefore, consider using a lightweight woven fusible or a tricot. A firm nonwoven interfacing should not be used since it would be too stiff and not drapey enough.

There are some premade fusible interfacings that can be purchased by the roll to use in certain areas of the garment. These easy-to-use interfacings are perfect for the fronts of blouses, waistbands, or cuffs. Some interfacings come with perforated guidelines, which makes sewing them easy for the operator.

Some factories order their own, custom-made, nonwoven fusible interfacing in various widths. They use the interfacing in garment areas that need particular reinforcement, such as the zipper area. (See Figure 8–2.)

FIGURE 8–1

Nonwoven, fusible interfacing with perforated guidelines

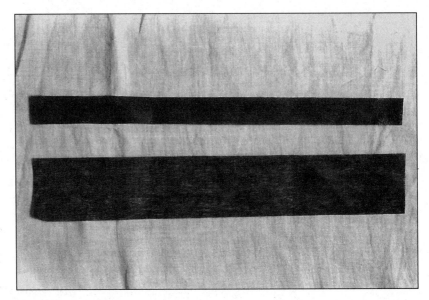

FIGURE 8–2

*Custom-made nonwoven
fusible interfacing*

Seam Reinforcement

In addition to interfacing, consider using **cold tape** to further reinforce seams and to prevent stretching, especially when topstitching your seams. Cold tape comes in three different widths: ¼″, ⅜″, and 1″. (See Figure 8–3.) The ⅜″ width is used most often.

Cold tape has a sticky back. Apply it before sewing the seams together, and use it on front openings, waistbands, zippers, cuffs, pocket openings, pocket flaps, collars, or any other place where extra support is needed.

Some applications for cold tape are on the edge of a waistband (Figure 8–4), the stitching line of a zipper (Figure 8–5), and the edge of a cuff (Figure 8–6). Additional uses for cold tape will be discussed in later chapters.

FIGURE 8–3

Three widths of cold tape

FIGURE 8–4

Cold tape on waistband edge

FIGURE 8–5

Cold tape on stitching line of a zipper

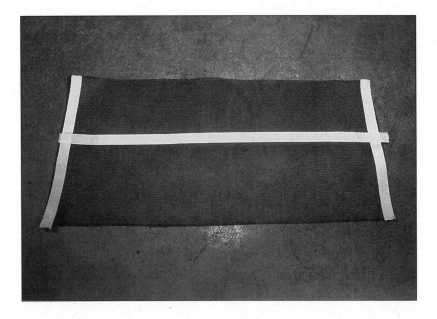

FIGURE 8–6

Cold tape on the edge of the cuff

Seam Finishes

Beginner sewers should not attempt to sew leather and suede. If a mistake is made, it will be difficult to hide resewn areas. Often, the garment will be ruined entirely because ripping out the seams in a poorly sewn leather garment can irreparably damage the skins, which can become costly.

Experienced sewers still should practice on leather or suede swatches before tackling "the real thing." This is a particularly good way to learn how to set a zipper, make a bound buttonhole, or welt a pocket.

Leather edges do not necessarily have to be finished since, unlike fabric, they do not unravel. Generally, allot a ½″ seam allowance, unless the design requires otherwise. The only real exception to this rule pertains to collars, where a ¼″ seam allowance should be alloted.

Although there are not many edging options, there are several seam options. The three most common types of seams include open and glued, mock flat fell, and raw edge lapped and stitched. A discussion of these three types of seams follows.

Open and Glued Seam

STEP ONE: Stitch seam. if the seam is curved, clip into the seam allowance no closer than ⅛″ to the stitching line. (See Figure 9–1.) If clipped any closer than this, the garment may tear when it is worn. Nonstress seams, such as collars and pocket flaps, can be clipped more closely.

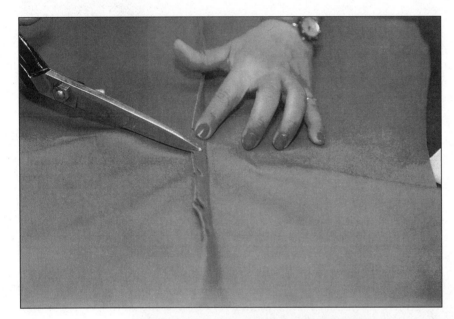

FIGURE 9–1

Step 1: Stitch and clip seams

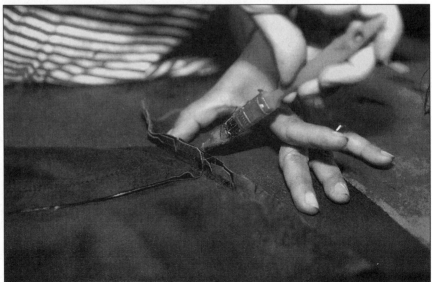

FIGURE 9–2

Step 2: Glue seam allowance

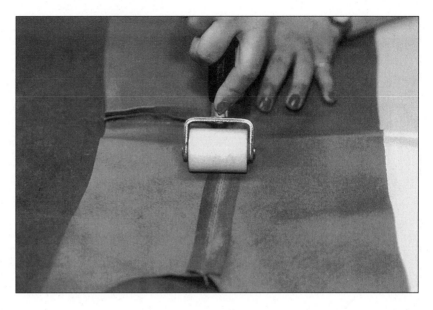

FIGURE 9–3

Step 3: Roll seam flat

STEP TWO: Using a small paint brush, apply glue to the seam allowance and gently press the seam allowance open and flat. (See Figure 9–2.)

STEP THREE: With a roller tool, apply pressure and roll the seams flat and smooth. (See Figure 9–3.)

Mock Flat Fell Seam

STEP ONE: Stitch seam.

STEP TWO: Push seam allowances to one side and topstitch to the body. Here, there is an option to edgestitch, double needle stitch, or even triple needle topstitch the seam. Figure 9–4 illustrates the use of edgestitching.

For double and triple needle seams, trim the seams when they are sewn together to reduce excess bulk, resulting in a step effect. This is often used on more expensive garments. For an example of double needle topstitching, see Figure 9–5.

To properly trim seams:

1. Sew the seam.
2. Push the seam allowance to one side.

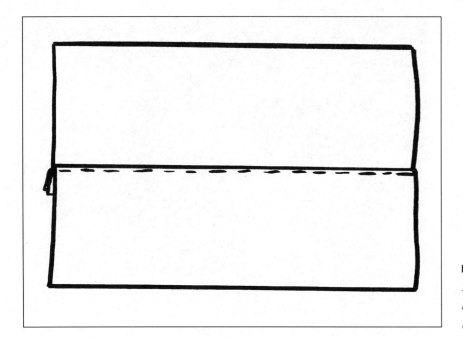

FIGURE 9–4

Mock flat fell with edgestitch. (Courtesy of Andre Croteau)

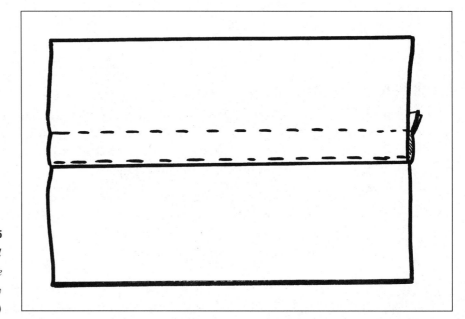

FIGURE 9–5

Mock flat fell double needle topstitch. (Courtesy of Andre Croteau)

3. Sew the first edgestitch.

4. Trim the upper seam allowance by ¼″.

5. Stitch the second edgestitch to create the double needle effect (or a third stitch for a triple needle effect). For the result, see Figure 9–6.

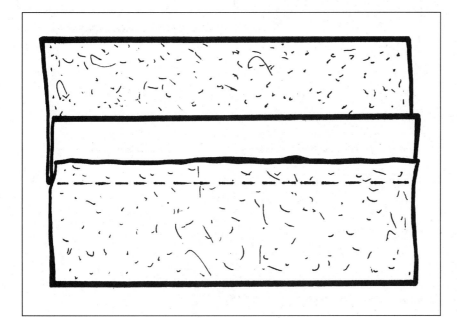

FIGURE 9–6

Trimmed mock flat fell seam. (Courtesy of Andre Croteau)

Raw Edge Lapped and Stitched Seam

STEP ONE: Start with an even-edged seam. The edge can be pinked for a decorative effect. Cold tape the wrong side on the edge to prevent stretching while topstitching. For a single stitched lap, leave a ¼″ seam allowance (see Figure 9–7) to create an edgestitched effect.

For a double stitched lap, allow for ½″ seam allowance (see Figure 9–8).

STEP TWO: Lap one seam on top of the other.

STEP THREE: Topstitch ⅛″ from the raw edge.

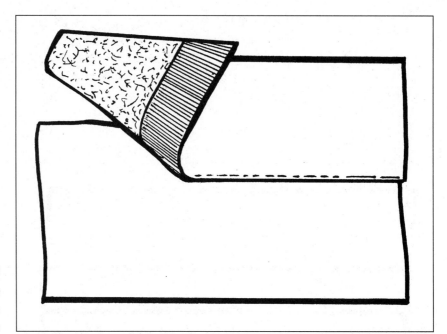

FIGURE 9–7

Single stitched lap seam. (Courtesy of Andre Croteau)

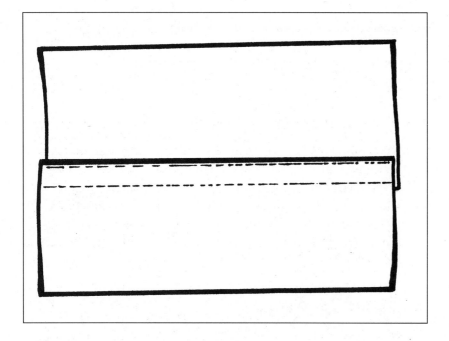

FIGURE 9–8

Double stitched lap seam. (Courtesy of Andre Croteau)

Sewing a Shirt

The Construction of a Shirt

This chapter covers the steps involved in constructing a shirt. The construction techniques involved are collar and collar stand setting, facing applications, sleeve setting, lining insertion, pocket construction, seaming, and topstitching. (See Figure 10–1.)

STEP ONE: Cold tape the center front panels, sleeve hem, and pocket. (See Figure 10–2.)

STEP TWO: Interface center front, sleeve hem, collar, collar stand, and front facing pieces. (See Figures 10–3 and 10–4.)

STEP THREE: Join together the upper and lower pieces of the front facings, shirt front, and shirt back. Also, join the two-piece sleeve together. Then glue open all seams and roller them flat.

STEP FOUR: Prepare the pocket by gluing the seam allowance, bending the seam allowance back, and hammering the edge flat. (See Figure 10–5.)

STEP FIVE: Place paper under the shirt front for ease when sewing the pocket to the body. (See Figure 10–6.)

STEP SIX: Stitch the pocket to the body. Do not backtack. Pull the threads through to the wrong side and double knot them. (See Figure 10–7.)

STEP SEVEN: Join the shoulder seam together with cold tape, open, glue, and roller flat.

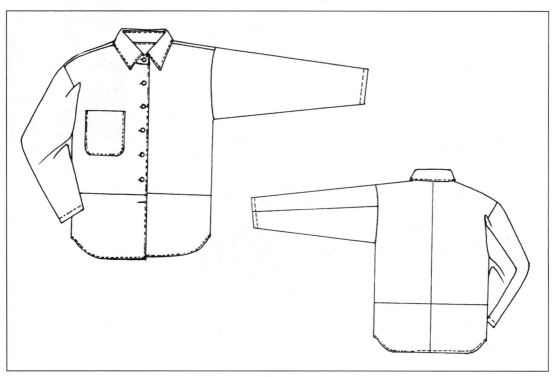

FIGURE 10–1

Front and back view. (Courtesy of Andre Croteau)

FIGURE 10–2

Applying cold tape to center front panels, sleeve hem, and pocket top

FIGURE 10–3

*Interface center front
and sleeve hem.*

FIGURE 10–4

*Interface collar, collar stand,
and front facing pieces.*

FIGURE 10–5

*Glue seam allowance of pocket
and hammer edge flat.*

FIGURE 10–6

Place paper under shirt front when sewing pocket to body.

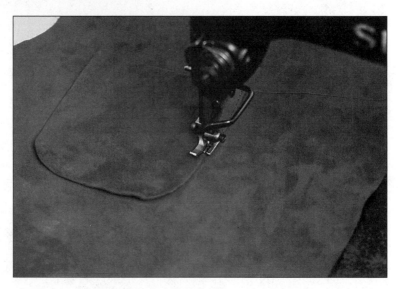

FIGURE 10–7

Stitch pocket to body.

STEP EIGHT: Sew the upper and under collar together, turn, trim, clip, and hammer the edge flat. (See Figure 10–8.)

STEP NINE: Stitch the collar together before joining it to the collar stand.

STEP TEN: Backstitch the collar stand. (See Figure 10–9.)

STEP ELEVEN: Stitch the collar stand together before setting it into the neckline. (See Figure 10–10.)

FIGURE 10–8

Hammer collar edge flat after joining upper and under collar together.

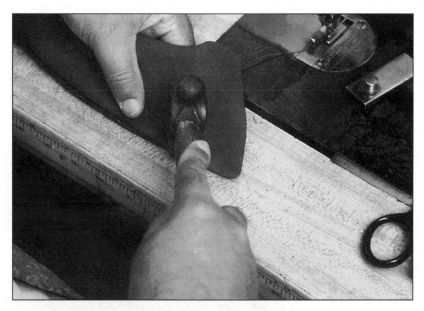

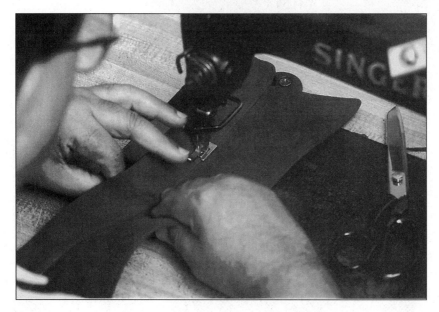

FIGURE 10–9

Backstitch collar stand.

STEP TWELVE: Trim the ends of the collar stand before setting it into the neckline to avoid excess bulk. (See Figure 10–11.)

STEP THIRTEEN: Sew the lining and front facing together, then stitch the front and back shoulder of the lining.

STEP FOURTEEN: Join the collar/collar stand and neckline together. (See Figure 10–12.)

STEP FIFTEEN: Attach the front facing/lining to the shirt, beginning about three inches down from the center front. Stitch around the neck, then down the center front.

FIGURE 10–10

Stitch collar stand together at neckline before setting it into neckline.

FIGURE 10–11

Trim ends of collar to avoid bulk.

FIGURE 10–12

Join collar, collar stand, and neckline together.

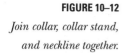

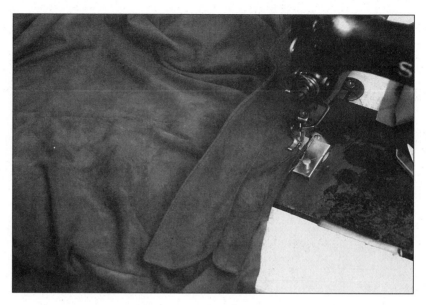

STEP SIXTEEN: Backstitch the facing all around. (See Figure 10–13.)

STEP SEVENTEEN: Thoroughly clip the neckline seam allowance. (See Figure 10–14.)

STEP EIGHTEEN: Close the front and back side seams and sleeve inseams. Open, glue, and roller flat.

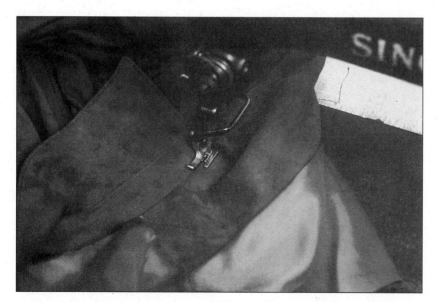

FIGURE 10–13

Backstitch facing around neckline.

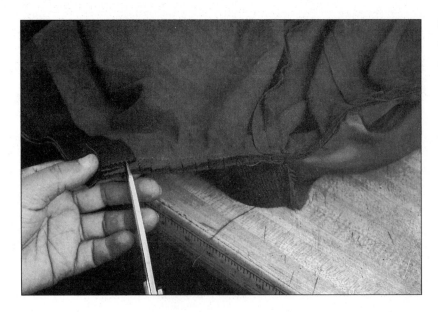

FIGURE 10–14

Clip neckline seam allowance.

STEP NINETEEN: Set the sleeve into the armhole and clip the seam allowance.

STEP TWENTY: Glue, then hem, the sleeve. Topstitch, if desired.

STEP TWENTY-ONE: Glue the shirt seam allowance hem. Then turn up and roller the hem. (See Figure 10–15.)

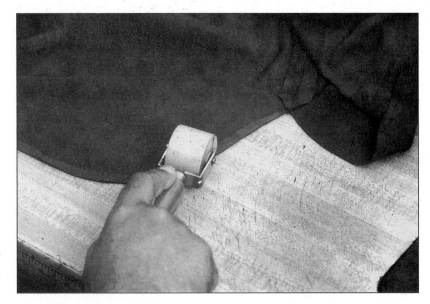

FIGURE 10–15

Glue shirt hem up and roller flat.

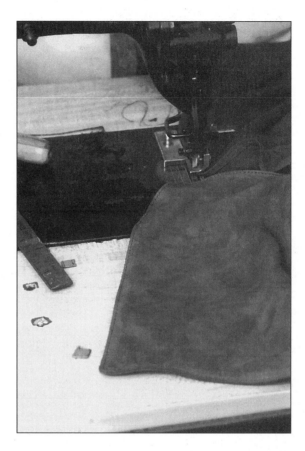

FIGURE 10–16

Edgestitch around center front and hem.

STEP TWENTY-TWO: Edgestitch the front edge around the shirt hem. Make sure there is enough top and bobbin thread in the machine before topstitching. (See Figure 10–16.)

STEP TWENTY-THREE: Glue the facing to the body.

STEP TWENTY-FOUR: Sew the lining to the armhole. The armhole lining can be overlocked before stitching or a bias binding can be applied after attaching the lining to the armhole of the body.

STEP TWENTY-FIVE: If bound buttonholes are desired, they must be added before step seven. Refer to the bound buttonhole instructions in the jacket section of this book. (See Chapter 12, Sewing a Jacket.) Machine-made buttons or snaps also are suitable. Buttons and button tacks should be hand sewn with a glover's needle.

STEP TWENTY-SIX: Press well.

Sewing a Pair of Pants

The Construction of a Pair of Pants

There are many different styles of pants, however, a pleated pant is one of the most popular. This style incorporates many elements that are common to other styles of pants, such as jeans. This chapter deals with the construction of the fly front, seaming, crotch sewing, zipper setting, darts, pockets, pleats, lining, loops, and waistband. (See Figure 11–1.)

STEP ONE: Sew the pleats. Then cold tape the waist, pocket welt, pant fly seam, fly pieces, and waistband. (See Figure 11–2.)

STEP TWO: Join the leg seams and glue them open.

STEP THREE: Interface the pant waistband, fly front, pocket opening, welt, and fly extension. (See Figure 11–3.)

STEP FOUR: Prepare pockets by slashing each pocket open and clip into the corners. (See Figure 11–4.)

STEP FIVE: Glue the pocket seam allowances open and hammer them flat. (See Figures 11–5 and 11–6.)

STEP SIX: Prepare the pocket welt pieces and fly extension by gluing them. Then fold them in half and roller press them flat.

FIGURE 11–1

*Front and back of
finished pants*

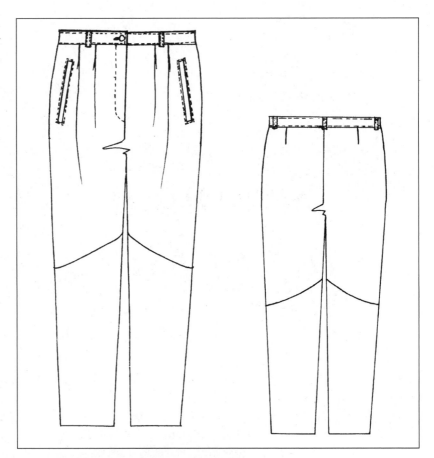

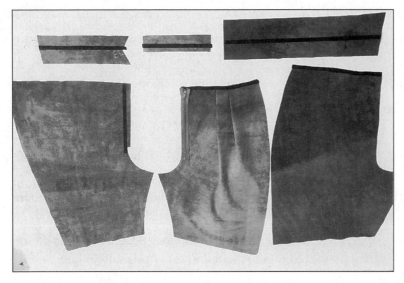

FIGURE 11–2

*Cold tape applied to pant
waistline, waistband, and
pant fly extension*

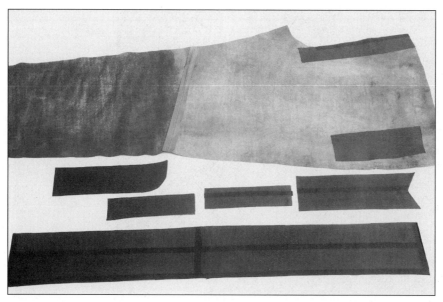

FIGURE 11–3

Interface pant waistband, center front, pocket area, pocket welt, and fly extension.

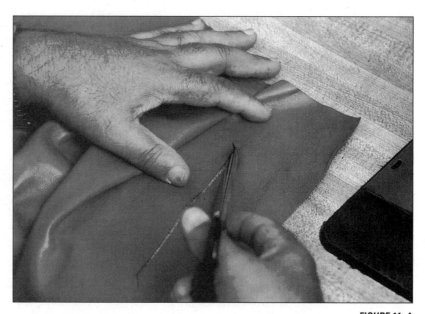

FIGURE 11–4

Slash open pocket and clip into corners.

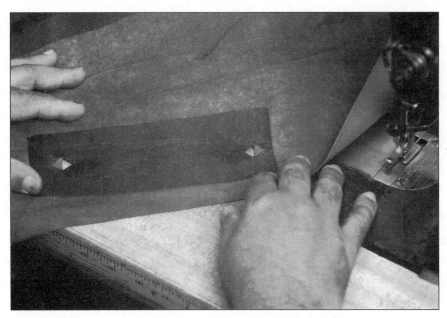

FIGURE 11–5

Open and glue pocket seam allowance.

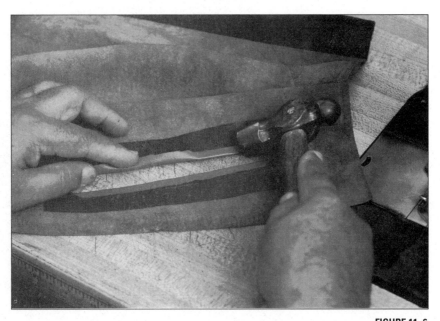

FIGURE 11–6

Hammer pocket seam allowance flat.

STEP SEVEN: Attach the pocket facing and pocket welt to the pocket lining and backstitch each of them. (See Figure 11–7.)

STEP EIGHT: Stitch the upper and lower pockets together. (See Figure 11–8.)

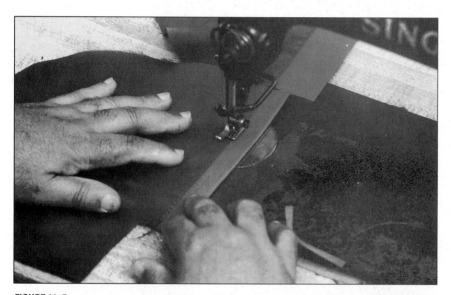

FIGURE 11–7

Attach pocket facing and pocket welt to lining, then backstitch.

FIGURE 11–8

Stitch upper and lower pocket together.

STEP NINE: Place the pant front over the pocket bag. (See Figure 11–9.)

STEP TEN: Fold down the lower pocket facing while topstitching the pocket to the pant on three sides. (See Figure 11–10.)

FIGURE 11–9

Place pant front pocket opening over pocket bag.

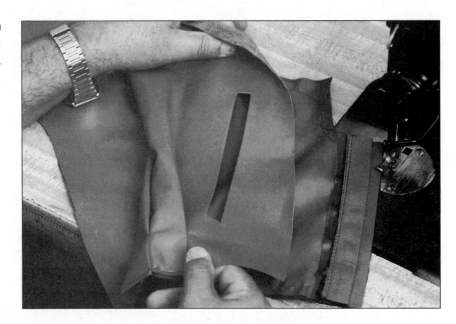

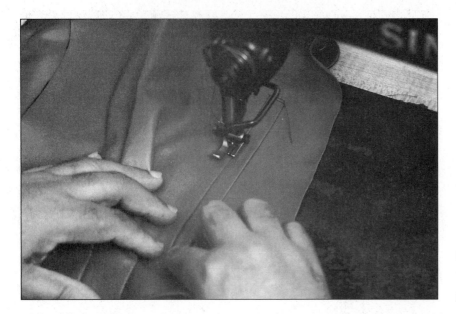

FIGURE 11–10

Topstitch pocket to pant on three sides.

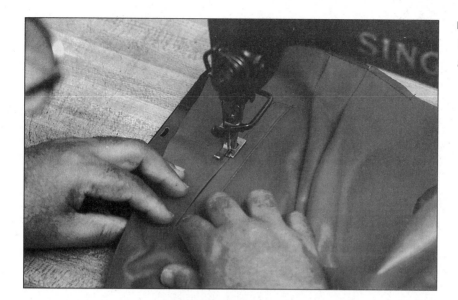

FIGURE 11–11

Topstitch last side of the pocket to the pant.

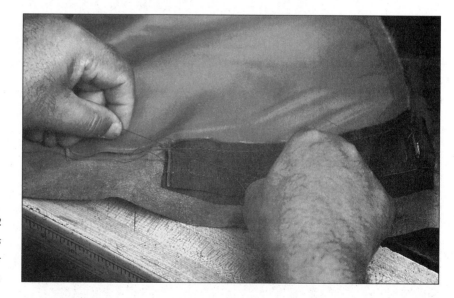

FIGURE 11–12

Double knot threads on wrong side after topstitching.

STEP ELEVEN: Flip the lower pocket up and topstitch the last side of the pocket to the pant. (See Figure 11–11.)

STEP TWELVE: Do not backtack or clip threads after sewing. Instead, pull threads through to the back and double knot. (See Figure 11–12.)

FIGURE 11–13

Prepare belt loops.

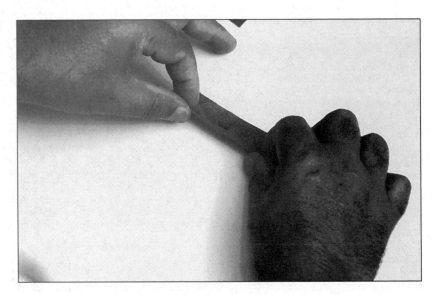

STEP THIRTEEN: Complete the pocket by stitching the pocket bag top and bottom.

STEP FOURTEEN: Prepare belt loops by gluing the loop, folding over ¼″, and folding again to make a ⅜″ wide loop. Then press flat. (See Figure 11–13.)

STEP FIFTEEN: Edgestitch each side of the belt loop and trim off the seam allowance close to the edge. (See Figure 11–14.)

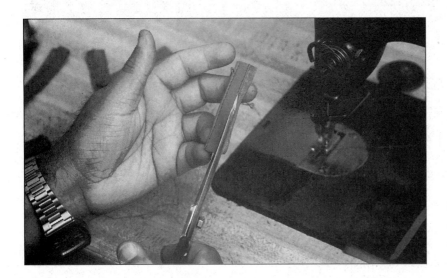

FIGURE 11–14

Edgestitch belt loop edges and trim seam allowance close to edge.

STEP SIXTEEN: Sew the curved fly facing to the pant. Then turn and backstitch. (See Figure 11–15.)

STEP SEVENTEEN: Sew the zipper to the fly facing. (See Figure 11–16.)

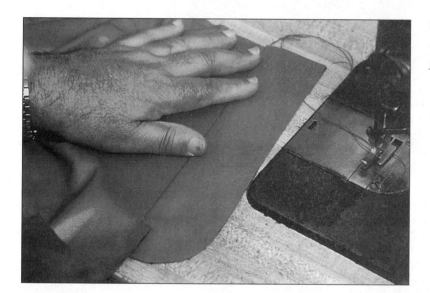

FIGURE 11–15
Backstitch fly facing after joining to pant.

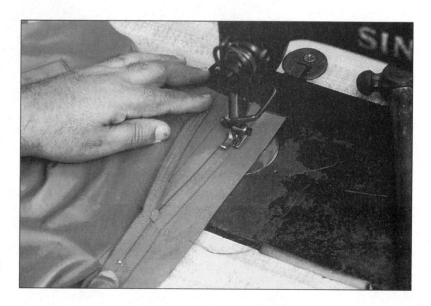

FIGURE 11–16
Sew zipper to fly facing.

FIGURE 11–17
Glue fly facing to pant.

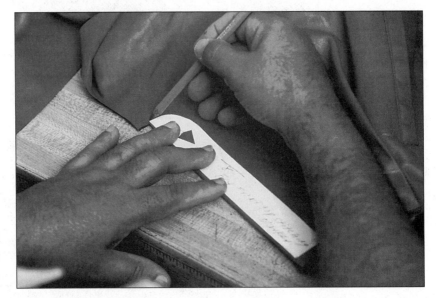

FIGURE 11–18
*Mark topstitch edge
with template.*

STEP EIGHTEEN: Glue the fly facing to the pant. (See Figure 11–17.)

STEP NINETEEN: Using a template, mark lightly with a pencil and topstitch. (See Figures 11–18 and 11–19.)

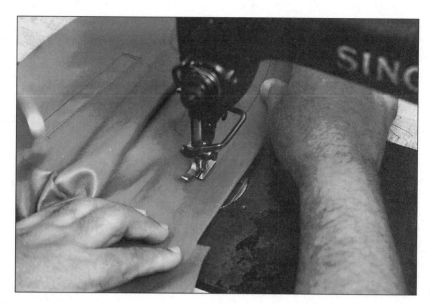

FIGURE 11–19

Topstitch fly front.

STEP TWENTY: Stitch the zipper to the left facing. (See Figure 11–20.)

STEP TWENTY-ONE: Starting at the base of the zipper on the left side of the pant, turn back a ½″ seam allowance and stitch the zipper to the pant close to the zipper teeth. (See Figure 11–21.)

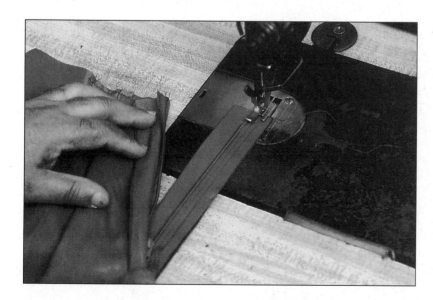

FIGURE 11–20

Stitch zipper to left facing on edge of zipper tape.

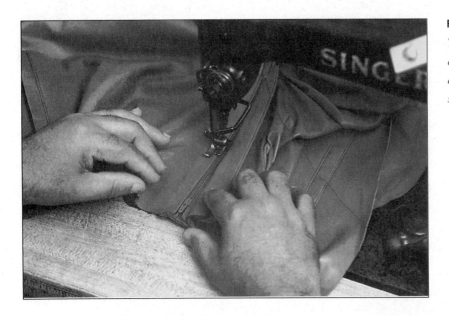

FIGURE 11–21

Turn back ½" seam allowance and edgestitch zipper to left side to fly.

STEP TWENTY-TWO: Cold tape the front crotch on one side and sew the two fronts together, beginning at the crotch and extending to the base of the zipper. Clip the crotch all around. (See Figure 11–22.)

FIGURE 11–22

Cold tape front crotch on one side while joining two fronts together.

STEP TWENTY-THREE: Cold tape and stitch the back crotch. (See Figure 11–23.)

STEP TWENTY-FOUR: Clip the crotch and glue the seams open. (See Figure 11–24.)

FIGURE 11–23

Cold tape and join back crotch together.

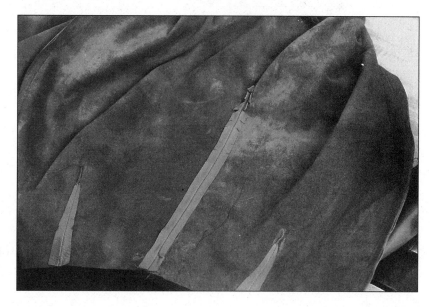

FIGURE 11–24

Clip around crotch and glue seams open.

FIGURE 11–25

Sew back darts, glue open, and roller flat.

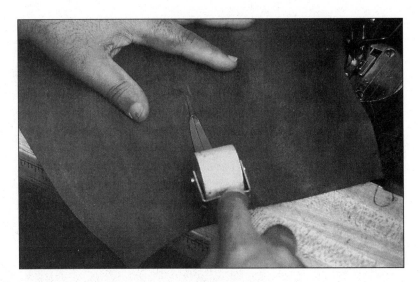

FIGURE 11–26

Make buttonhole on waistband.

STEP TWENTY-FIVE: Sew the back darts, glue them open, and roller them flat. (See Figure 11–25.)

STEP TWENTY-SIX: Sew the side seams and inseams open, glue, and roller them flat.

STEP TWENTY-SEVEN: Make the buttonhole on the waistband See Chapter 12, Sewing a Jacket, for buttonhole sewing instructions. (See Figure 11–26.)

STEP TWENTY-EIGHT: Sew the lining together.

STEP TWENTY-NINE: Glue the edges of the center front seam allowance on the waistband. (See Figure 11–27.)

STEP THIRTY: Attach the lining to the fly extension on the left side. (See Figure 11–28.)

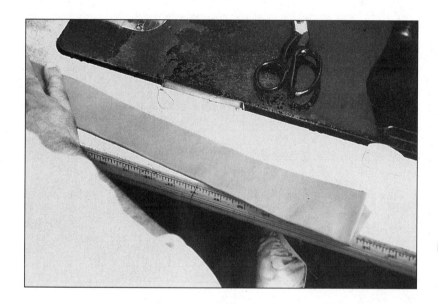

FIGURE 11–27

Glue seam allowances on center front waistband.

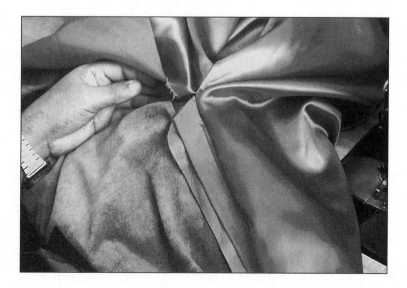

FIGURE 11–28

Attach lining to fly extension on left side.

STEP THIRTY-ONE: Attach the lining to the right side of the fly facing, catching the left side of the fly extension. (See Figure 11–29.)

STEP THIRTY-TWO: Stitch the lining to the pant at the waistband. (See Figure 11–30.)

FIGURE 11–29

Attach lining to right side of fly facing, catching left side of fly extension.

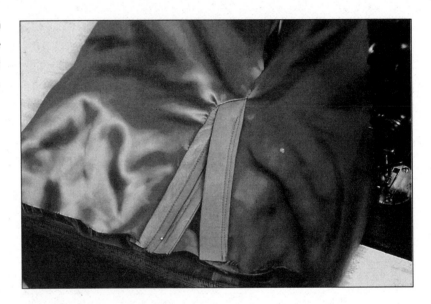

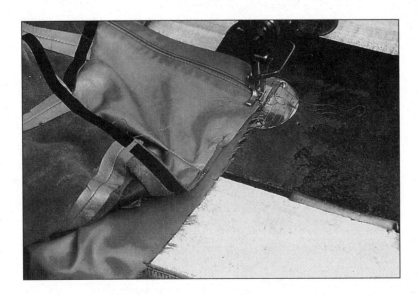

FIGURE 11–30

Stitch lining to pant at waistband.

STEP THIRTY-THREE: Trim the edge on the waistband close to the seamline to eliminate bulk at the point. (See Figure 11–31.)

STEP THIRTY-FOUR: Align the belt loops to the waistband while joining
the waistband to the pant waist. (See Figure 11–32.)

FIGURE 11–31

*Trim edge on waistband
close to seamline to
eliminate bulk.*

FIGURE 11–32

*Align belt loops to
waistband while joining
waistband to pant waist.*

FIGURE 11–33
Hammer waistband edge flat.

STEP THIRTY-FIVE: Fold over the waistband center edge and hammer it flat. (See Figure 11–33.)

STEP THIRTY-SIX: Beginning at the front belt loop, edgestitch the waistband all around. (See Figure 11–34.)

FIGURE 11–34
Edgestitch waistband beginning at front loop.

STEP THIRTY-SEVEN: Catch the upper loop as you topstitch the upper edge of the waistband. (See Figure 11–35.)

STEP THIRTY-EIGHT: Trim the waistband seam allowance on the inside. (See Figure 11–36.)

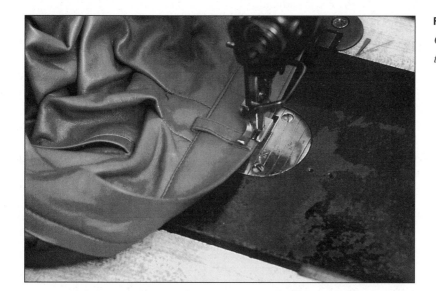

FIGURE 11–35

Catch loop while topstitching waistband.

FIGURE 11–36

Trim waistband seam allowance on inside.

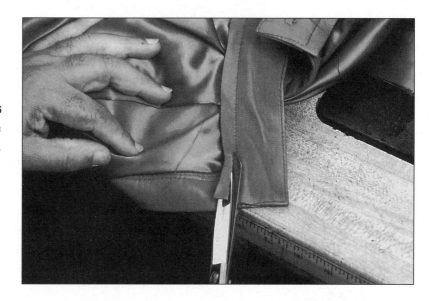

STEP THIRTY-NINE: Machine topstitch the hem of the lining.

STEP FORTY: The pant hem can be glued and turned up or glued and topstitched.

STEP FORTY-ONE: Sew the button on with a glover's needle, using a button tack reinforcement.

STEP FORTY-TWO: Press well.

Sewing a Jacket

The Construction of a Jacket

This chapter describes all of the steps involved in constructing a jacket. (See Figures 12–1 and 12–2.)

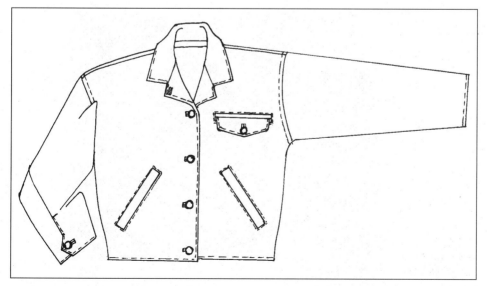

FIGURE 12–1

Jacket front

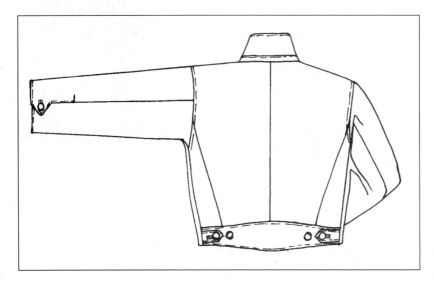

FIGURE 12–2

Jacket back

PREPARING INTERFACINGS

STEP ONE: Place all the leather parts to be interfaced face up on the gummed side of the tricot interfacing. (See Figure 12–3.)

STEP TWO: Interface the sleeve cuff and the centerfront of the jacket. (See Figures 12–4 and 12–5.)

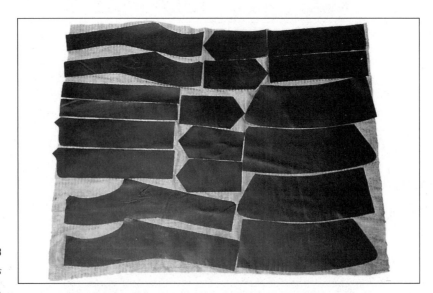

FIGURE 12–3

Place leather parts on interfacing.

FIGURE 12–4

Interface the cuff.

FIGURE 12–5

Interface the centerfront.

PREPARE AND SEW BUTTONHOLES

STEP THREE: Prepare the buttonhole welts by cutting the pieces 2″ wide for a 1″ wide button (or 1″ wider than the width of the button). (See Figure 12–6.)

STEP FOUR: Open all buttonhole markings on all parts containing buttonholes. Be careful to slit the "V" carefully. (See Figure 12–7.)

STEP FIVE: Sew the buttonhole welt corners to the body. (See Figure 12–8.)

FIGURE 12–6

Prepare buttonhole welts.

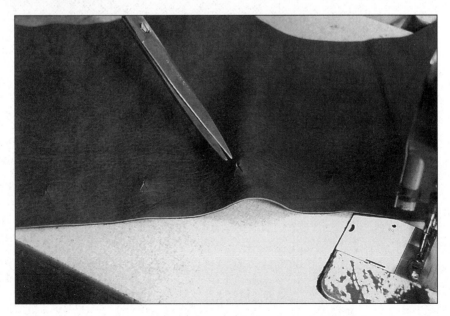

FIGURE 12–7

Open all buttonhole markings.

FIGURE 12–8

Sew buttonhole welts.

STEP SIX: Complete the buttonhole by sewing across the welt. (See Figures 12–9 and 12–10.)

STEP SEVEN: Trim the inside edges of the buttonhole welt. (See Figure 12–11.)

STEP EIGHT: Hammer the finished buttonhole flat. (See Figure 12–12.)

FIGURE 12–9

Complete the buttonhole (Step 1).

FIGURE 12–10

Complete the buttonhole (Step 2).

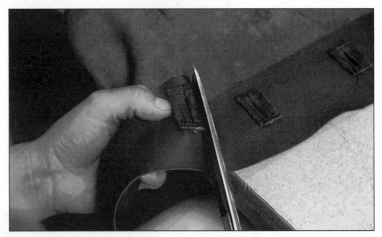

FIGURE 12–11

Trim inside edges of welt.

FIGURE 12–12

Hammer the finished buttonhole.

PREPARE AND SEW FLAPS AND TABS

STEP NINE: Using a template, mark the corners of the sleeve opening. (See Figure 12–13.)

STEP TEN: Using a template, mark and sew the pocket flaps. (See Figure 12–14.)

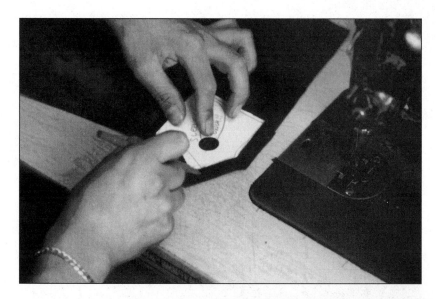

FIGURE 12–13
Mark corners of sleeve opening.

FIGURE 12–14
Mark and sew pocket flaps.

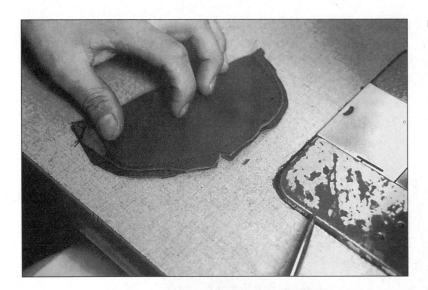

FIGURE 12–15

Trim the pocket flap and notch out the point.

FIGURE 12–16

Turn the pocket and hammer the edge.

STEP ELEVEN: Trim the pocket flap in a stepwise fashion and notch out the point. (See Figure 12–15.)

STEP TWELVE: Turn the pocket and hammer its edge. (See Figure 12–16.)

STEP THIRTEEN: Edgestitch the pocket all around the flap. (See Figure 12–17.)

FIGURE 12–17

Edgestitch pocket.

STEP FOURTEEN: Crackstitch on the inside of the buttonhole. (See Figure 12–18.)

STEP FIFTEEN: Using a template, mark, then stitch, the tab. (See Figure 12–19.)

FIGURE 12–18

Crackstitch on the inside of the buttonhole.

STEP SIXTEEN: Trim and notch out the points of the tab. (See Figure 12–20.)

STEP SEVENTEEN: Turn, edgestitch, and hammer tabs.

FIGURE 12–19

Mark, then stitch, the tab.

FIGURE 12–20

Trim and notch out points of tab.

WELT POCKET PREPARATION AND SEWING

STEP EIGHTEEN: Slit the pockets carefully and glue them down. (See Figure 12–21.)

STEP NINETEEN: Hammer the pocket opening once it is glued. (See Figure 12–22.)

FIGURE 12–21

Slit and glue pockets.

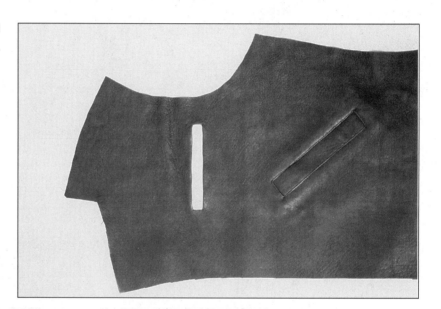

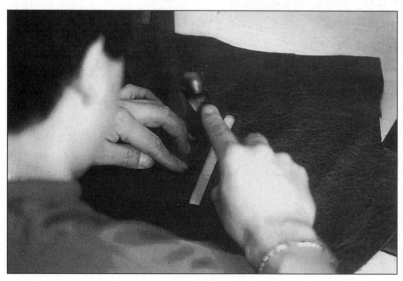

FIGURE 12–22

Hammer pocket opening.

FIGURE 12–23

Prepare welt (Step 1).

STEP TWENTY: Prepare welt by gluing the piece. (See Figures 12–23 and 12–24.)

STEP TWENTY-ONE: Hammer the welt flat. (See Figure 12–25.)

STEP TWENTY-TWO: Sew the pocket facing and welt to the pocket lining. (See Figure 12–26.)

FIGURE 12–24

Prepare welt (Step 2).

FIGURE 12–25

Hammer welt.

FIGURE 12–26

Sew pocket facing and welt to lining.

STEP TWENTY-THREE: Join pocket linings together, beginning at the welt seam allowance, to the same point on the other side. (See Figure 12–27.)

STEP TWENTY-FOUR: Line up the pocket bag to the pocket opening. (See Figures 12–28 and 12–29.)

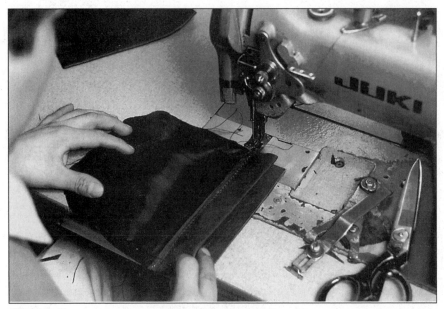

FIGURE 12–27

Join pocket linings together.

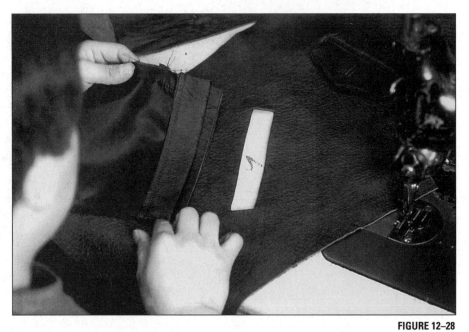

FIGURE 12–28

Line up pocket bag (View 1).

STEP TWENTY FIVE: Starting in the corner, stitch on the top all around the edge of the pocket opening of the welt section. Be sure to fold down the pocket facing side first, then flip up to complete the topstitch. (See Figure 12–30.)

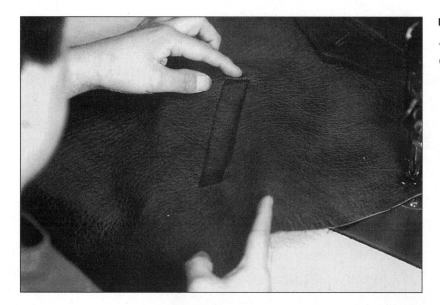

FIGURE 12–29

Line up pocket bag (View 2).

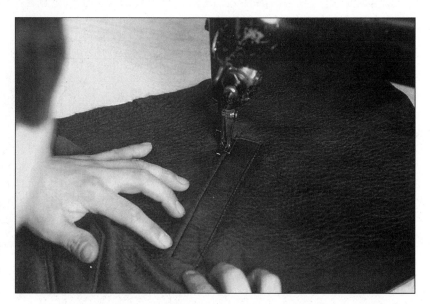

FIGURE 12–30

Stitch around the edge of the pocket opening.

BISOM POCKET WITH FLAP PREPARATION AND SEWING

STEP TWENTY-SIX: Prepare the welts and pocket lining in the same way the welt pocket was prepared above. Join the two welt pieces together by stitching them on the sides. (See Figure 12–31.)

STEP TWENTY-SEVEN: Line up the pocket bag with the slit. (See Figure 12–32.)

FIGURE 12–31

Prepare welts and pocket lining.

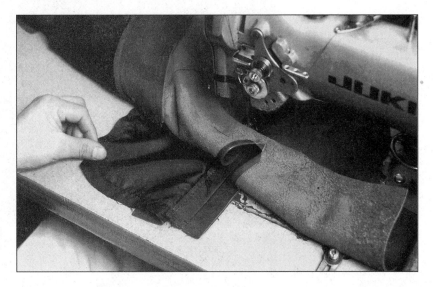

FIGURE 12–32

Line up the pocket bag with the slit.

FIGURE 12–33

Fold down the facing side.

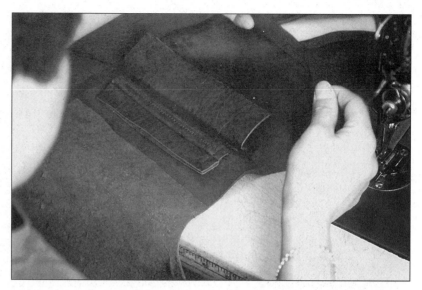

STEP TWENTY-EIGHT: Be sure to fold down the facing side before stitching the lower side of the pocket. (See Figure 12–33.)

STEP TWENTY-NINE: Start stitching in the lower pocket corner. (See Figure 12–34.)

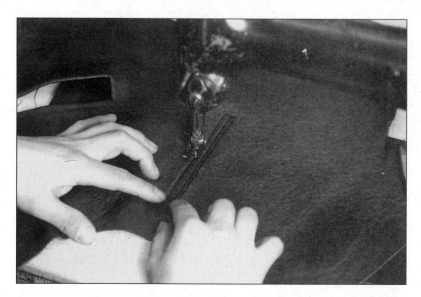

FIGURE 12–34

Start stitching in the lower pocket corner.

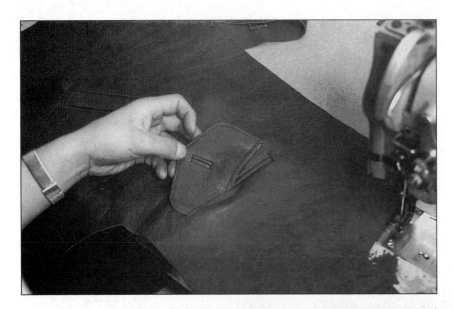

FIGURE 12–35

*Insert pocket flap into
upper pocket opening.*

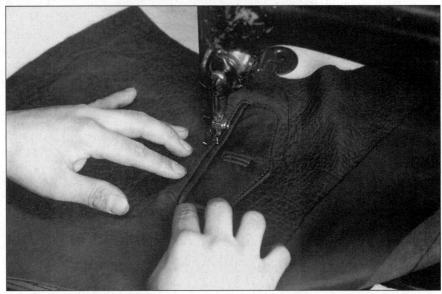

FIGURE 12–36

*Continue to
topstitch pocket.*

STEP THIRTY: Insert the pocket flap into the upper pocket opening and continue to topstitch. Be sure to flip up the pocket facing at this time. (See Figures 12–35 and 12–36.)

STEP THIRTY-ONE: Hammer the pocket flap and bisom pocket. (See Figure 12–37.)

FIGURE 12–37
*Hammer pocket flap
and bisom pocket.*

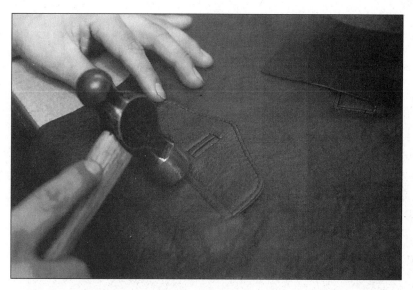

FIGURE 12–37
*Hammer pocket flap
and bisom pocket.*

SEWING THE BODY OF THE GARMENT AND WAISTBAND

STEP THIRTY-TWO: Join the center back seam.

STEP THIRTY-THREE: Join the back waistband piece to the jacket back. Fold the pleat as you sew. (See Figure 12–38.)

FIGURE 12–38
*Join the back waistband
piece to the jacket back.*

STEP THIRTY-FOUR: Join the waistband facing to the waistband and edgestitch on the waistband. (See Figure 12–39.)

STEP THIRTY-FIVE: Place the tabs on the waistband side seam and stitch. (See Figure 12–40.)

STEP THIRTY-SIX: Close the side and shoulder seams.

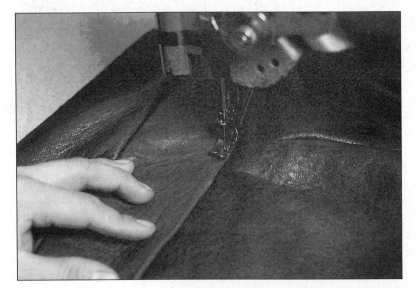

FIGURE 12–39

Join and edgestitch the waistband.

FIGURE 12–40

Place the tabs on the waistband side seam and stitch.

COLLAR AND COLLAR STAND PREPARATION AND SEWING

STEP THIRTY-SEVEN: Join the under collar pieces together. (See Figure 12–41)

STEP THIRTY-EIGHT: Join the under collar to the collar stand. (See Figure 12–42.)

FIGURE 12–41

Join under collar pieces.

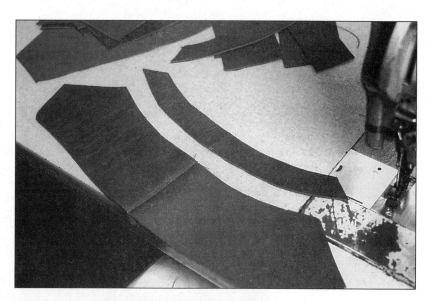

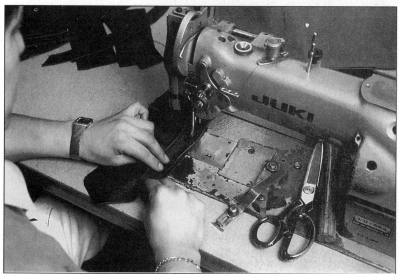

FIGURE 12–42

Join under collar to collar stand.

FIGURE 12–43

Edgestitch on collar stand.

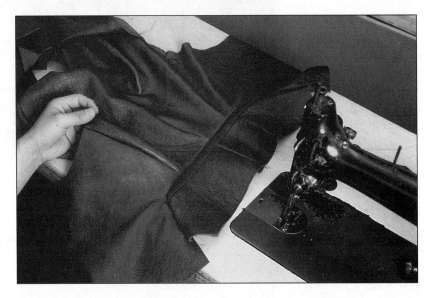

FIGURE 12–44

Join under collar to body of jacket.

STEP THIRTY-NINE: Edgestitch on the collar stand. (See Figure 12–43.)

STEP FORTY: Join the under collar to the body of the jacket. (See Figure 12–44.)

STEP FORTY-ONE: Glue all of the inside seams open. (See Figure 12–45.)

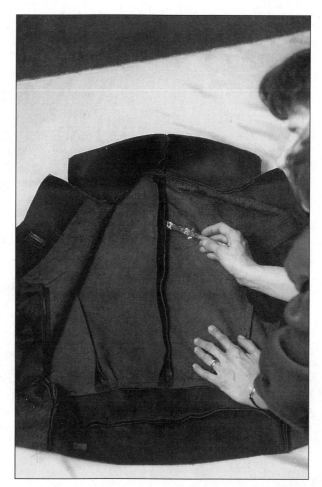

FIGURE 12–45

Glue all inside seams open.

FRONT FACING AND TOP COLLAR PREPARATION AND SEWING

STEP FORTY-TWO: Join the front upper to the lower facing. (See Figure 12–46.)

STEP FORTY-THREE: Sew the collar stand to the upper collar.

STEP FORTY-FOUR: Sew the collar to the front facing. (See Figure 12–47.)

STEP FORTY-FIVE: Clip and open all corners. (See Figure 12–48.)

FIGURE 12–46

Join front upper and lower facing.

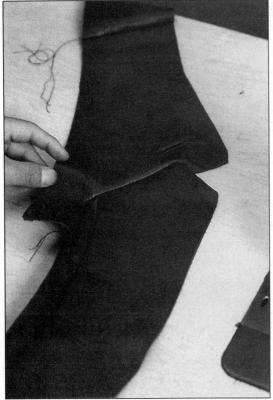

FIGURE 12–47

Sew collar to front facing.

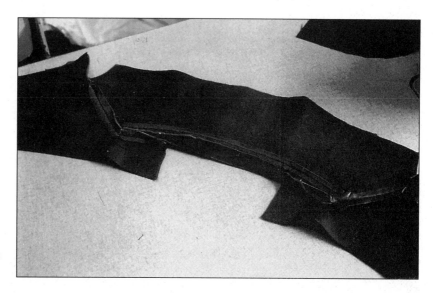

FIGURE 12–48

Clip and open all corners.

SLEEVE AND SLEEVE WRIST DETAIL

STEP FORTY-SIX: Join the two sleeve pieces together.

STEP FORTY-SEVEN: Sew the sleeve facing to the sleeve. (See Figure 12–49.)

FIGURE 12–49

Sew sleeve into armhole.

STEP FORTY-EIGHT: Clip and trim the sleeve facing. (See Figure 12–50.)

STEP FORTY-NINE: Turn, hammer, and edgestitch the sleeve facing. (See Figure 12–51.)

STEP FIFTY: Sew the sleeve into the armhole. Clip into the seam allowance all around. (See Figure 12–52.)

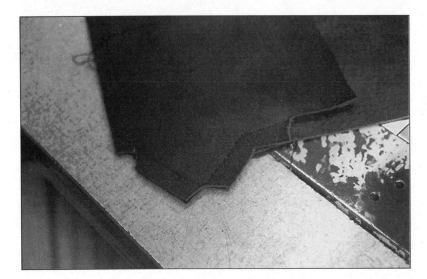

FIGURE 12–50

Clip and trim sleeve facing.

FIGURE 12–51

Turn, hammer, and edgestitch sleeve facing.

FIGURE 12–52

Sew sleeve into armhole.

FIGURE 12–53

Sleeve detail complete

STEP FIFTY-ONE: Figure 12–53 shows the completed sleeve.

STEP FIFTY-TWO: Stitch the shoulder pad to the shoulder seam. (See Figure 12–54.)

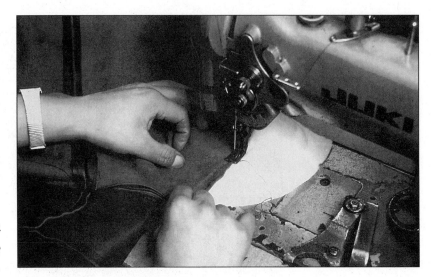

FIGURE 12–54

Stitch shoulder pad to shoulder seam.

FRONT FACING AND LINING

STEP FIFTY-THREE: Cold tape the center front of the body, collar, and hem.

STEP FIFTY-FOUR: Join the front facing to the hem on one side only.

STEP FIFTY-FIVE: Start sewing the facing to the body, about 3″ down from the lapel point. (See Figure 12–55.)

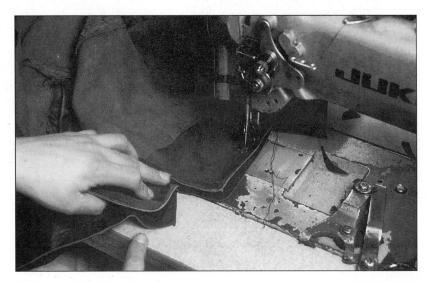

FIGURE 12–55

Sew facing to body.

Continue to sew around the collar to 3″ down from the lapel point on the other side; then stop and compare both the left and right fronts. Trim if the lengths are uneven. Sew the facing to the hem and then complete the front facing.

STEP FIFTY-SIX: Clip the corners of the facing and trim the seam allowance in a step-wise fashion. (See Figures 12–56 and 12–57.)

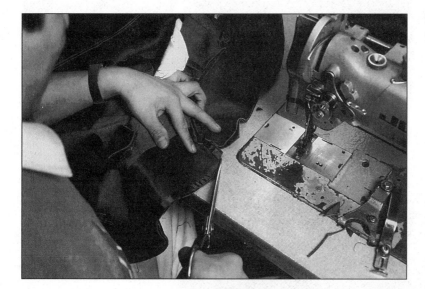

FIGURE 12–56

Trim the corners of the facing.

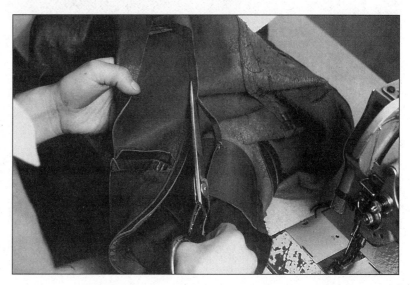

FIGURE 12–57

Trim the seam allowance of the facing.

FIGURE 12–58

Trim the seam allowances.

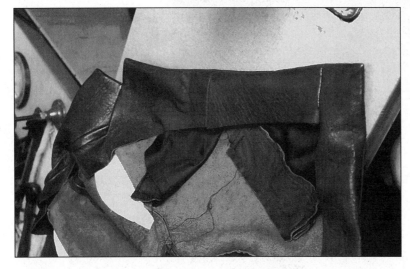

FIGURE 12–59

Hammer collar edge and front edge.

STEP FIFTY-SEVEN: Trim the seam allowances on the hem/facing seam to reduce bulk. (See Figure 12–58.)

STEP FIFTY-EIGHT: Turn the collar and facing. Hammer the collar edge and the front edge. (See Figure 12–59.)

STEP FIFTY-NINE: Sew a ¼″ topstitch all around the edge of the jacket. (See Figure 12–60.)

FIGURE 12–60

Sew a ¼″ topstitch.

STEP SIXTY: Sew the lining together. Leave a 10″ opening in the sleeve inseam so the garment can be turned inside out later.

STEP SIXTY-ONE: Join the lining to the body at the hem. (See Figure 12–61.)

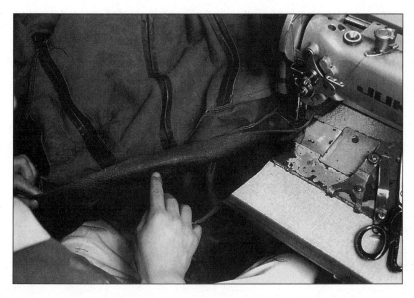

FIGURE 12–61

Join lining to body at hem.

STEP SIXTY-TWO: Join the lining from the hem to the top of the lapel on both sides. (Figure 12–62.)

STEP SIXTY-THREE: Sew the lining to the neckline. (See Figure 12–63.)

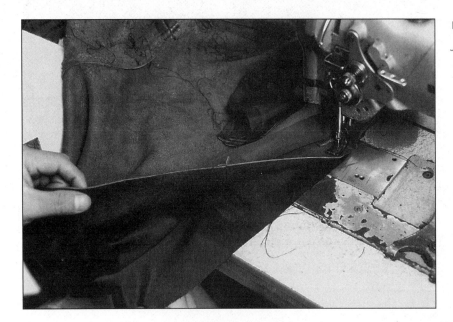

FIGURE 12–62

Join lining from hem to top of lapel.

FIGURE 12–63

Sew lining to neckline.

FIGURE 12–64

Sew sleeve lining to sleeve wrist opening.

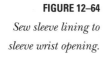

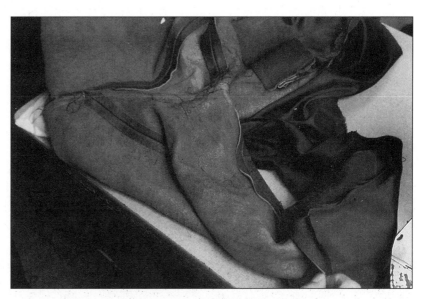

FIGURE 12–65

Machine stitch the 10-inch opening on sleeve lining inseam.

STEP SIXTY-FOUR: Sew the sleeve lining to the sleeve wrist opening. (See Figure 12–64.)

STEP SIXTY-FIVE: Turn garment inside out and machine stitch closed the 10″ opening in the sleeve lining inseam. (See Figure 12–65.)

STEP SIXTY-SIX: Now, the jacket lining is complete. (See Figure 12–66.)

STEP SIXTY-SEVEN: Slit all of the buttonholes with a short knife. (See Figure 12–67.)

STEP SIXTY-EIGHT: Sew the buttons together with a button tack reinforcement using a glover's needle.

STEP SIXTY-NINE: Press the jacket well.

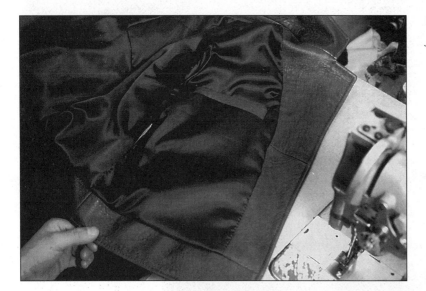

FIGURE 12–66

Jacket lining complete

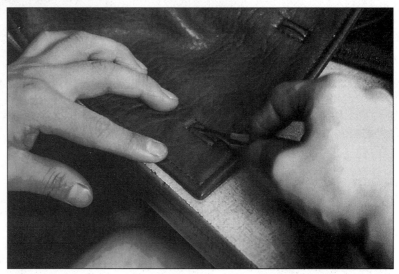

FIGURE 12–67

Slit all buttonholes with a short knife.

Leather Defects

The Importance of Independent Testing

Garment leather can be obtained in approximately seventy countries throughout the world. However, tanneries may sell skins with serious physical problems. This chapter provides advice about how to identify and solve many of the most common quality control problems that are encountered with finished, full-grain garment leathers and suede.

While many tanneries test their skins before they ship them to manufacturers, many do not. It should be a routine procedure to test skins that are bought before cutting them. (Figure 13–1 shows an example of a leather test report.)

One of the best testing labs in the world is the Leather Industries Research Laboratory at the University of Cincinnati. Much of the lab's experience is based on diagnosing problems with completed garments, as well as raw skins.

The Leather Industries Research Laboratory is the only independent leather testing lab in the United States. Many of the biggest leather garment manufacturers, as well as top United States retailers, send their skins or finished garments to this lab for testing.

Frank H. Rutland, the former Technical Director of the Leather Industries Research Laboratory, has contributed most of the information on leather testing in this chapter.

FIGURE 13–1

KOREA MERCHANDISE
TESTING & RESEARCH INSTITUTE
459-28 Kasan-Dong, Kumcheon-Gu, Seoul, Korea
Tel: (02)856-5615-17, 19. Fax: (02)856-5618, 854-6667

TEST REPORT

NO.: 8121   DATE: Nov. 24, 1995
CLIENT: KUMHUNG LEATHER CO., LTD.
SAMPLE DESCRIPTION: Cowhide Grain Leather
TEST RESULTS:

TESTS CONDUCTED		RESULTS	TEST METHOD
Dynamic waterproofness Test			SATRA PM 34
– Water Penetration (min)		17	
– Water Absorption (%)		52	
Tensile Strength (kgf)		17.2	BS 3144
Tearing Strength (kgf)		6.8	BS 3144
Shrinkage Temperature (°C)		135	BS 3144
pH Value		3.7	KS M 6882
Colorfastness to Drycleaning (Class)			BS 1006
– Change in color		4	Part D01
Staining (cotton)		2	
Colorfastness to Rubbing (Class)			BS 1006
– Dry (200 Cycle)	Change in Color	4–5	Part UK-LG
	Staining (Wool Felt)	4–5	
– Wet (50 Cycle) ;	Change in Color	4–5	
	Staining (Wool Felt)	3–4	
Colorfastness to Light (class)		Over 4	AATCC 16A

Sample

Signed by _____

         For   Tack Won Kwon
               President

FIGURE 13–1

Example of a leather test report from Korea.

Skin, Hide and Leather Defects by Jean J. Tancous also should be read for additional descriptions and illustrations of leather quality control problems and solutions.[1]

There are no uniform standards or industry specifications for garment leather in the United States. Product criteria are generally established between buyers and sellers through the evaluation and acceptance of initial production samples. Therefore, the recommendations made in this chapter are solely based upon the considerable experience of the Leather Industries Research Laboratory and should not be taken as representative of actual industry standards.

How to Identify and Solve Key Quality Control Problems

COLOR PROBLEMS

FADING. Many people believe fade resistance is relatively unimportant for garment leathers, since garment and product life cycles and exposure times are usually relatively short.

However, there are times when fade resistance can be quite important, such as when items need to be displayed for a prolonged period of time in a sunlit retail display window.

Frank H. Rutland of the Leather Industries Research Laboratory reported that he once received a pair of black suede shoes in which the right shoe only had turned a reddish-brown. His lab demonstrated that the color change in the right shoe was due to light fading of a blue dye component in the leather. The lab speculated that the right shoe was taken out of the box at some point for display purposes.

If an expensive leather garment is to be displayed in a sunlit window, potential fading problems can be checked by sending the garment to a lab. The lab will probably test the garment for fade resistance in a carbon arc or equivalent fadeometer. Ideally, the garment should demonstrate that it can endure a minimum of twenty-four hours exposure with negligible color change.

CROCKING. **Crocking** refers to the physical transfer of color through a rubbing action, which can be a rather serious problem with some garment leathers.

---

[1] Available from the Shoe Trades Publishing Company.

To a large extent, tanners can minimize crocking by choosing proper dyes and effecting the right dyeing conditions when they process skins. However, since crock-fast dyes and dye fixation procedures are generally more expensive, tanners may make compromises to economize. This is particularly true for some tanners outside of the United States.

Crocking can be tested under either dry or wet conditions by rubbing the leather with a standard test cloth and then evaluating the degree of color transfer, using a standard chromatic transference scale (ASTM Method D 5053).[2] For good crocking resistance, testing labs look for values that are no lower than 4.0 dry and 3.5 to 4.0 wet, based on the AATCC Chromatic Transference Scale.

Suede leather poses additional crocking problems. It not only transfers dye, as described above, but it also transfers small dyed fibers which have broken off during the suede buffing process. Tanners can eliminate the problem by properly de-dusting skins following buffing.

BLEEDING OR STAINING. **Bleeding** (or **staining**) is the familiar problem that can occur when colored and white laundry is mixed in the washing machine. It refers specifically to the migration of dye in a solution from the leather into another material. It is a condition that can be caused by perspiration, laundering, or wet weather exposure and is largely controlled by the tanner's choice of dye and dyeing conditions.

To anticipate the color bleeding or staining potential of a garment before customers discover the problem first, submit a sample of the leather to a qualified testing lab before manufacturing. The lab will probably test the skin by pressing the leather against a wet test cloth and the evaluate the degree of color transfer (ASTM Method D 5552). Test results should be comparable to those for crocking resistance.

STRENGTH

In general, leather has exceedingly good properties of strength, which makes the material more than sufficient for most end-use

---

[2]References to standard test methods for leather in this chapter refer to either the ASTM (American Society for Testing and Materials) or Federal Test Method Standard No. 311 (General Services Administration).

applications. As a result, strength failure in leather articles is relatively uncommon.

However, since some garment leathers are quite thin, manufacturers occasionally run into strength problems, particularly in the area of stitch tear strength.

One of the most common causes of low tear strength is **over-splitting**, that is, splitting a thick hide into pieces of leather that are too thin. This is of particular concern with cattle hide garment leather. Most of the strength in an animal skin is the interior (corium) of the skin, not the outside or grain layer. If too much of the corium layer is removed during splitting, the leather is not only weakened but the hand and softness also are adversely affected. This condition can be detected microscopically if the thickness of the corium layer has been reduced to less than half of the total leather's thickness.

Stitch tear strength also can be measured directly (ASTM Method D 4705) but quantitative results are directly proportional to leather thickness. Considering this, the Leather Industries Research Laboratory has not identified a single desired test value that is independent of thickness. In general, the laboratory believes that tensile strength (ASTM Method D 2209), which takes leather thickness into account, is a good surrogate test for most strength parameters. For garment applications, the laboratory recommends a minimum tensile strength value of 2,500 pounds per square inch.

ABRASION RESISTANCE

In general, the abrasion or wear resistance of leather is quite good. For finished leathers, the actual level of abrasion resistance is to a large degree determined by the type of finishing system used on the skins and can be controlled to a reasonable degree by the tanner through the use of appropriate finish formulations.

For lightly finished or aniline leathers, there is little that can be done to improve wear resistance. In garments made with such leather, excess water is most likely to occur on turned edges (e.g., cuffs, hem lines, etc.) where the leather is highly stretched and most exposed. This property can be tested using a Taber Abrasion Tester (ASTM Method D 3384). With CS-10 wheels and a 500 gm weight per wheel, the Leather Industries Research Laboratory looks for no evidence of finish wear (other than the possible dulling of the finish luster) after 1,000 wheel cycles.

FINISH ADHESION

Finished leather, much like finished furniture, occasionally flakes or peels. This is of particular concern with garment leather, which is subjected to a high degree of flex.

Poor finish adhesion is clearly a manufacturing problem that can result from improper finish formulations and a high oil and grease content in the leather. Manufacturers can quickly test for finish adhesion by administering what is known as the Scotch Tape Test.

Simply adhere a piece of Scotch Tape to the finished surface of a skin, then sharply pull it off. If any finish is removed and remains stuck to the tape, there may be a finish adhesion problem.

Finish adhesion can be measured quantitatively in the laboratory by sticking a test strip to the finished surface of the leather then measuring the force required to peel the finish from the leather (European test method). This test is rarely performed in the United States, and there is not an equivalent ASTM method at this time. More commonly, finished adhesion is determined by measuring the flex resistance of leather. Although there are several test machines, one of the most common is the Bally Flexometer®. Using this instrument, the Leather Industries Research Laboratory recommends that a skin stand up to a minimum of 60,000 flexes without producing visible finish cracks that permeate the surface of the leather.

BLOCKING. Another finish-related problem is known as **blocking**, which is the adhesion of a leather finish to itself. Federal Test Method 3121.1 tests for this condition by folding a piece of leather and holding it together, grain-to-grain, under heat, humidity, and pressure, so that the finish surface is in contact with itself. If the testing lab cannot separate the two leather grain surfaces without finish damage, the leather is said to block.

Blocking also is a finish formulation problem. It can be problematic during those applications (e.g., upholstery) where leather is likely to be in contact with itself under perpetual pressure and at elevated temperatures and humidity. Blocking is a property of the finish top-coat system and is distinct from tackiness. **Tackiness** exists whenever leather feels tacky or sticky and will adhere to almost anything it touches. Tackiness is usually due to the inadequate drying or curing of the finish system.

Obviously, it goes without saying that good garment leather should be free of blocking.

CORROSION RESISTANCE

As discussed in detail in Chapter 3, the tanning process makes leather slightly acidic, with a pH of 5.0 and sometimes less. This is quite normal and is not likely to cause any type of manufacturing or consumer problem. However, if the leather is too acidic, which occasionally happens, and is placed in direct contact with unprotected, corrodible metals (e.g., buttons, rivets, zippers, etc.), the leather can corrode the metal.

To avoid this, the Leather Industries Research Laboratory recommends that leather pH should always be greater than 3.5 (ASTM Method D 2810). In addition, corrodible metal trim (e.g., parts made of iron or copper) should have some type of surface protection.

The corrosion resistance of leather can be measured directly by holding it in direct contact with a metal test block for a prolonged period of time during elevated humidity, then observing if there is any test block corrosion (ASTM Method D 1611).

SHRINKAGE

One of the most common complaints manufacturers and dry cleaners hear from customers is that their leather garments have shrunk following commercial dry cleaning.

The cleaning industry has issued reports from testing laboratories that blame shrinkage problems on manufacturers' use of poor-quality hides.

In fact, shrinkage is exclusively a problem with the cleaning process itself. Specifically, shrinkage occurs when cleaners allow excessive temperatures and mechanical agitation to occur during the cleaning process. This is because leather protein fibers, like many textile fibers, are subject to shrinkage if exposed to high temperatures under wet conditions.

This fact must be taken into account when cleaning a leather garment. It is primarily for this reason that it is strongly recommended that leather garment cleaning be done only by a qualified professional leather cleaner and not by an ordinary dry cleaner that is inexperienced in leather care.

OIL SPOTTING/SOILAGE

Leather is a highly absorbent material, thus leathers with little or no surface finish protection will readily absorb skin oil. Over time, this will darken the color of the leather. This is especially noticeable around the inside of a leather collar.

Unfortunately, oil spotting and soilage is quite common in aniline and lightly finished leathers. These types of leathers generally require more frequent cleaning.

Manufacturers can avoid this problem by sewing a protective lining inside the collar during the manufacturing of the garment. They also may avoid or minimize the problem by selecting skins that have been specially tanned. In recent years, newer tannages have been developed that are highly oil and water resistant and, in some cases, even launderable.

There also are a number of customer-applied, leather care products on the market designed to provide a greater degree of oil repellency in leather garments. (See Appendix C, Resource Directory.)

SPEW

Occasionally some leather will develop a white hazy deposit on its surface. This deposit is known as **spew** or **fatty spew**.

The condition is more likely to occur in colder weather and can be confirmed if the spew disappears after gently warming.

Most leathers contain significant amounts of fat and oil that act as natural lubricants for their protein fibers. In finished tanned skins, there commonly will be a combination of natural animal fat and additional oils supplemented by the tanner.

In soft garment-type leathers, the oil content may be as high as 20 to 30 percent. Some of the fat and oil components that are not "fixed" to the hide protein may migrate to the surface of the leather and solidify if their melting point is above ambient temperature conditions.

Spew usually appears as a whitish hazy film. Although it can be readily wiped away, it will probably redevelop at the right temperature.

Gentle warming will cause the spew to melt and penetrate the leather, but this solution usually is not permanent. A light treatment with a suitable fat solvent offers a more permanent solution. However, this should only be done by a trained professional, since many solvents are toxic and there is a real danger of the solvent's causing permanent damage to the skin's leather finish.

The only way to totally avoid spewing is to purchase properly tanned skins treated with an optimized oil formulation system.

MOLD/MILDEW

Leather's proteins and associated fats and oils provide an excellent medium for fungal growth under damp conditions. Therefore, care needs to be exercised during the handling and storage of leather garments.

Leather that has become wet should be allowed to dry slowly, at room temperature, without adding any artificial heat.

Leather should be stored in a dry, well-ventilated area, not under damp conditions (e.g., a damp basement), which is a sure invitation to mildew.

It should always be allowed to breath and should not be stored in plastic garment bags. A garment bag sometimes can act like a greenhouse, providing the perfect conditions for mold or mildew growth.

Existing mold and/or mildew can be easily eliminated by wiping the leather with a damp cloth, if caught early enough. More serious cases of mildew can be corrected by spraying the skin or garment with a very fine mist of commercial fungicide (e.g., Lysol®). However, this must be done very carefully to avoid spotting the leather or damaging the finish. Wherever possible, test such a treatment in a hidden area of the garment. If all else fails, the garment should be taken to a qualified, professional leather cleaner.

WATER SPOTTING

Certain aniline or lightly finished leathers may be susceptible to water spotting. This condition occurs when leather contains oils, dyes, or other components that are water-soluble. Once these components go into solution in water, they tend to migrate to the perimeter of the wetted area. When the leather dries and the spotting components come back out of solution, they often leave a distinctly visible ring.

There is very little that can be done to solve this type of problem, other than keep the leather as dry as possible. Some commercial after-market products that improve surface repellency may prove helpful, but these too need to be carefully tested in a hidden part of the garment as they may negatively affect the aesthetic properties of the leather.

Manufacturers would be best advised to buy skins that have been produced using some of the newer oil/water resistant tannages mentioned earlier.

ODOR

The natural proteins in hides have only a slight odor. But the oils and some of the processing chemicals used in the tanning process impart a characteristic "leather" smell to leather products. Generally, most people find this odor quite agreeable.

Occasionally, however, customers may complain about noxious odors. Sometimes these complains are simply due to the fact that some people are very sensitive to certain smells. However, some "medicinal" leather odor problems are associated with the use of chlorinated phenolic preservatives during the tanning process. These additives are designed to prevent bacterial/fungal attack. Although banned for use in the United States for almost ten years, these materials are still legally available in other areas of the world and may be present in some imported leathers.

There is one other source of distasteful leather odor which, although it is quite rare today, is worth mentioning. The tanning process has evolved significantly over the years. Most of today's tanners use entirely clean, modern chemicals. However, this has not always been the case. For example, some native tribes in remote areas of the world still use animal brains in the tanning process.

Before the era of modern tanning, hides were tested with the natural enzymes found in animal excrement, a process known as **puering**. This process is still employed in some underdeveloped areas of the world, and it is possible that some of these leathers have found their way into commercial manufacturing which could explain the existence of unpleasant leather odors.

LOOSE/PIPEY GRAIN

It is quite common for some garment leathers to evidence a **pipey grain**, that is, a loose, coarse, puckered appearance on the grain surface of an animal skin. Severe cases result from the actual separation of the grain layer from the inner corium layer. This condition is known as **double hiding**.

Pipey grain can be caused by bacterial damage, excessive chemical treatment during tannage, or excessive mechanical working of leather to produce a desired physical appearance.

Since garment leathers generally receive more chemical and mechanical treatment than shoe or accessory leathers to make them soft, they are more prone to suffer from pipey grain.

Some animal skins, such as sheepskins and goatskins, have a natural loosely attached grain, thus are more prone to double hiding. Also, the belly and pocket areas of most skins have a loose fiber structure than other parts of the skin. This makes those areas more prone to puckering.

Generally, the existence of pipey grain in a leather garment can be blamed on poor purchasing and/or cutting decisions made by the manufacturer. A manufacturer can easily see where skins are likely to pucker over time, after a cursory examination. By avoiding the inclusion of those areas in the raw skins of finished garments, future puckering problems can be avoided.

APPEARANCE VARIATIONS

Virtually all leather products exhibit some variation in grain character (in full grain leathers), nap character (in suede leathers), and color (in aniline leathers). These factors, along with surface blemishes, are natural variations that result from differences in the fiber structure within an individual hide or skin.

These differences are tied to a specific location on the skin (e.g., backbone versus belly), animal breed, age, sex, feed, and other environmental conditions, as well as seasonal factors. Variations in grain pattern, for example, are to cattle hide leather exactly what a cowlick is to a human being. Although such variations may be the bane of the leather cutter, they are part of what makes leather unique.

Sewing and Handling Ultrasuede® and Ultraleather®

Ultrasuede® and Ultraleather® Construction Techniques

In the late 1960s, the Japanese spent over seven years developing a synthetic fabric that would simulate suede leather. In the United States, the product is manufactured by Springs Industries under the registered trademark of Ultrasuede®.

Ultrasuede® is comprised of approximately 60 percent polyester and 40 percent nonfibrous polyester; it is manufactured using a nonwoven process.

While Ultrasuede® looks and feels much like real suede, a garment made of this material costs about one-fourth of the price of a comparable real suede garment. In addition, an Ultrasuede® garment will not shrink, fray, wrinkle, crock, stretch, or pill, and is machine washable.

Springs Industries currently make two types of Ultrasuede®: Ultralight®, which is 5.3 ounces per square yard and Ultrasuede® #223, which is 6.5 ounces per square yard. Their rolls are 45 inches wide and cost approximately $25 per yard wholesale. Ultrasuede® comes in approximately thirty-seven colors.

Springs Industries also makes a product known as Ultraleather®, made of 100 percent polyurethane with 70 percent cupramonium rayon and 30 percent nylon backing. Each roll is 48 inches wide and costs approximately $30 per yard wholesale. Ultraleather® comes in four colors.

While there are many variations of faux suede and leather in the marketplace, the sewing and handling techniques are the same for each.

YARDAGE REQUIREMENT

Ultrasuede® behaves much like fabric "with nap," such as velvet. Pieces should be cut to match the direction of the product's natural nap.

However, Ultraleather® can be cut both ways, just like any regular nonnap fabric.

CUTTING

Ultrasuede® must always be cut in the same direction. Cut with the nap up for a darker, richer look and cut with the nap down for a lighter, shinier look. All pattern pieces must be placed in the same direction. Ultraleather® can be cut in either direction. Use weights to hold the pattern down on the fabric with both Ultrasuede® and Ultralight®. Pins can be used but only in the seam allowance, since all pinholes will be permanently visible. Ultrasuede® and Ultraleather® can be cut with scissors. The fabric can be cut while folded, however the yield will be better when it is cut open.

MARKING

For marking, use a smooth-edged tracing wheel and dressmaker tracing paper or tailor's chalk. Darts may be marked with a chalk pencil or a small hole.

BASTING

All basting must be done in the seam allowance, since needle holes will remain in both Ultrasuede® and Ultraleather®. Fine pins should be used as well as doublefaced tape, however, do not use glue of any type.

TABLE 14–1 STITCH LENGTH AND NEEDLE SIZE				
	Fabric Needle Size	**Topstitch Needle**	**Stitch Length**	**Topstitch Length**
Ultralight®	#9–11 ballpoint	#9–14	11–13 per inch	8–11 per inch
Ultrasuede® and Ultraleather®	#11–14	#11–16	10–12 per inch	5–8 per inch

SEAM FINISHES

Seam allowances are usually ½ to ⅝ inches, except for any pattern pieces that are turned and trimmed or cleaned, such as collars, pocket flaps, epaulets, and so on. A ¼-inch seam allowance should be used for the latter pattern pieces.

Ultrasuede®, Ultralight®, and Ultraleather® edges will not fray. Therefore, it is not necessary to finish the edges.

There are three basic seam construction methods that should be used when sewing with Ultrasuede®-type products.

THE CONVENTIONAL SEAM

Here, the seam is sewn, opened, and pressed flat on the wrong side using a pressing cloth or a pounding block. (See Figure 14–1.)

Sometimes, it may be necessary to use a strip of doubleface fusible web (e.g., Crown-Armo) to hold the seams down flat. (See Figures 14–2 and 14–3.)

THE TOPSTITCHED SEAM

Here, the seam is sewn, opened, and topstitched flat. (See Figure 14–4.)

The seam also can be sewn, then one side is trimmed to create a graded seam effect. (See Figure 14–5.)

Or, all of the seam allowance is placed to one side and then topstitched. (See Figure 14–6.)

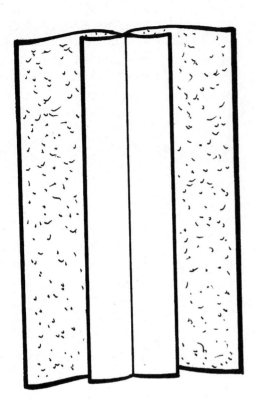

FIGURE 14–1

Conventional seam sewn,
opened, and pressed flat

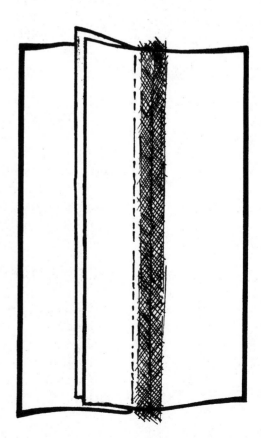

FIGURE 14–2

Placing doubleface fusible
strip to hold seams down

FIGURE 14–3

*Doubleface fusible web
holding seams down*

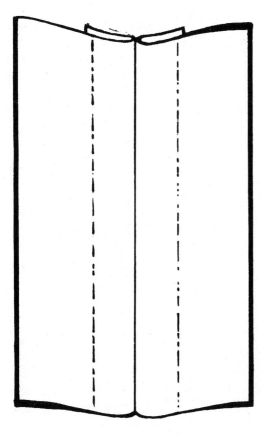

FIGURE 14–4

Seam opened and topstitched

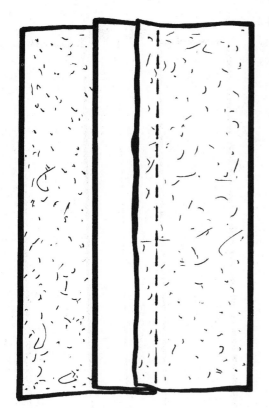

FIGURE 14–5

Graded seam effect

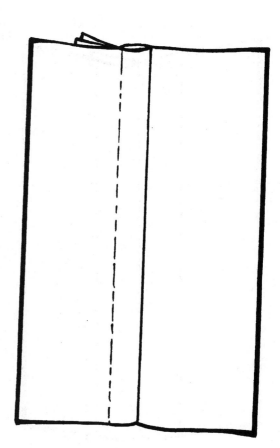

FIGURE 14–6

*All seam allowance placed to
one side, then topstitched*

THE LAPPED SEAM

Here, the raw edge is placed on top of the seam allowance, then topstitched for a sporty effect. (See Figure 14–7.)

Sometimes designers like to use a combination of seam finishes in the same garment, especially since crotch seams and armholes are better looking when sewn with a conventional seam finish.

HEM FINISHES

Ultrasuede®, Ultralight®, and Ultraleather® can be hemmed by using one of four methods.

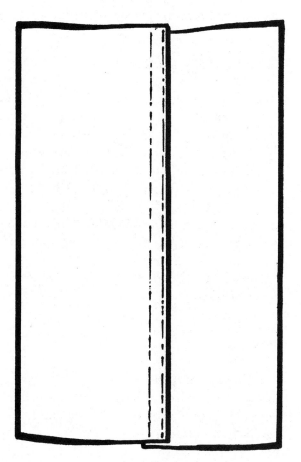

FIGURE 14–7

Lapped seam effect

1. Raw edge
2. Turned up and machine topstitched
3. Turned up and hand stitched or machine blindstitched
4. Turned up and held in place with a doublefaced fusible strip

THREAD

The best thread choice for all Ultrasuede® products is either 100 percent polyester or a cotton-wrapped polyester. For topstitching, two threads can be used, but a test swatch should first be used.

INTERFACING

Use a preshrunk fabric interfacing, such as Armo Weft® or Pellon Sof-Shape®. Fuse the interfacing to the wrong side of the fabric.

SPECIAL SEWING NOTES

A Teflon® sewing machine foot, plate, and teeth may be useful in helping the fabric glide through the machine.

Keep the machine top and bobbin tension eased.

Choose patterns and designs that are tailored and avoid styles with a lot of gathers and fullness. Ultrasuede® and Ultraleather® can only be eased about 1″ in 10″. Ultralight can be eased about ½″ in 10″.

Do not use too many darts. Make them as long as possible. Avoid dimpling at the point by trimming the fabric on the inside of the dart down to the point.

Reinforce dart points and crotch seams with a small piece of fusible interfacing.

LINING

Lining can be used to prevent the garment from stretching, to hide the inside construction of the garment, or to provide comfort. If a lining is going to be added, it should be a washable one if the garment is to be washed.

CARE AND CLEANING

Recommended care instructions for Ultrasuede® follow:

Machine wash/delicate cycle. Tumble dry/low setting, remove immediately. Use mild detergent without bluing agents, such as Ivory Snow® or Woolite®. Do not bleach. Hand wash/hang dry. Do not wring or twist. Wash alone to avoid color absorption from other garments. Brushing lightly will restore nap.

Advise purchaser to press their Ultrasuede® garment on the wrong side with a napped press cloth, a terry towel, or another piece of Ultrasuede® between the ironing board and the fabric. Strips of paper should be placed under the seam allowance to prevent an imprint on the right side. Purchasers should always set irons on a low synthetic setting. Ultraleather® can be pressed with a pressing cloth and at the same iron setting as Ultrasuede®. Steam may be used. Both fabrics can be dry cleaned.

To remove any unwanted pinholes, try steam pressing the garment and brushing it with a brush.

Ultrasuede® and Ultraleather® can be stored in plastic bags, unlike real leather garments. Store garments on padded or wooden hangers like any fine garment.

Leather Garment Care

A leather garment should be treated as any other fine garment, with a few exceptions:

1. Do not store the garment on a wire hanger. Always use a wide hanger to maintain the garment's shape.

2. Do not store leather garments in plastic bags or in a hot, bright, or damp room. Excess dryness may cause the leather to crack and moisture can cause mildew. Consider using cold storage during the summer months.

3. If a leather garment gets wet, allow it to air dry naturally, since quick drying near a radiator will cause the leather to dry out and crack.

4. A new leather garment can be pre-treated with a stain-repellent finish, which will help prevent stains from occurring.

5. Leather cleaners and conditioners are available in retail outlets to help restore leather garments to their original state after repeated wear. However, an excess buildup of these products can clog the pores in the leather, inhibiting the skin's ability to

breathe. Apple Brand Leather Care® is a light cleaner and conditioner that is easy to use and effective. Lexol® Brand cleaner and conditioner also is a good product. Note: All cleaners should be tested for staining on a small hidden area of the garment, for example, near the hem or under them collar.

6. Do not apply pins or adhesive tape to the surface of leather garments.

7. Avoid spraying perfume and hairspray directly onto a leather garment. In general, do not allow a garment to become exceedingly soiled, as this may cause permanent damage.

8. Do not attempt to remove difficult stains. Contact a qualified professional leather cleaner.

9. A hem can be fixed by applying a small amount of rubber cement to the area.

10. Iron a leather or suede garment by placing a heavy brown paper bag on top of it; use a low setting, with no steam.

11. Expect some color and texture changes after professional dry cleaning, even when performed by qualified professionals.

12. Garments may shrink after professional dry cleaning but will stretch out again with wear.

13. Wipe off dust and dirt on a leather garment with a soft dry sponge or cloth. Buy a special suede brush and buffing block to clean the surface of nu-buck and suede.

14. Only trust a professional leather dry cleaner to clean a leather garment. (See Appendix C, Resource Directory, for a list of leather cleaners.)

15. Do not send leather garments to the neighborhood dry cleaner unless they can demonstrate that large volumes of these garments are cleaned on a regular basis. Most local dry cleaners know a lot more about textiles than leathers. Do not consider cleaning a leather garment at a "coin op" dry cleaning location.

16. Women should consider wearing scarves when wearing delicate, difficult-to-clean leather garments, as scarves protect garments from cosmetics and body oils.

17. To remove a small minor stain use a large pencil eraser, but only after this process has been tested on the inner, unexposed facing of the garment to ensure the eraser does not damage the skin.

18. If a garment becomes wrinkled, put it on a hanger and gently pull the wrinkles out without significantly stretching the skin. If this fails, try to press the garment with an iron. First make sure the garment is totally dry. Place a heavy brown paper bag over the garment and keep the iron constantly moving over the paper. Set the iron on its lowest heat setting. Never use steam when ironing.